"It really works to have a mix of contri[butors?] the issues from all angles. So you've got t[he?] informative – and really important to he[lp?] but you're also hearing from people wit[h?] disorders, their family and carers, reinfor[c?] ery is always possible."

Stacey Dooley, *Author of* Are You Really O̶K̶.̶.̶ Understanding Britain's Mental Health Crisis, *UK*

"This book is an excellent combination of professional and lived experience voices resulting in a comprehensive and easily digested outline of eating disorders; an illness that is seldom well understood but which people do recover from, when treated. The authors eloquently explain important topics such as assessments, treatment, medical emergencies and the diversity of how eating disorders can affect anyone of any age. I recommend this book for health and school professionals as well as families and friends."

Professor Tim Kendall, *NHS Mental Health National Clinical Director, UK*

EATING DISORDERS

Eating disorders affect people from all backgrounds, and often go untreated for years. This book offers an accessible and evidence-based overview.

Chapters explore some of the most common risk factors that can predispose, precipitate, and perpetuate an eating disorder, as well as understanding the typical way they are diagnosed and treated. Interwoven with real life stories, and written by authors with diverse experiences, they provide the tools necessary to understand eating disorders better. Topics include anorexia nervosa, bulimia nervosa, binge eating disorder, treatment, diversity in eating disorders, and how to support someone living through these conditions. A glossary of useful key terms is included, along with chapter summaries and up-to-date research.

This book is essential for all health care professionals and students, as well as those suffering with an eating disorder and their families and friends.

Dr. Elizabeth McNaught is a GP, co-founder and medical director of Family Mental Wealth, UK.

Janet Treasure is a professor at King's College London and a consultant psychiatrist at the South London and Maudsley NHS Foundation Trust, UK.

Jess Griffiths is a therapist specialising in eating disorders and works as the national co-lead for FREED (First Episode Rapid Early Intervention for Eating Disorders) at the South London and Maudsley NHS Foundation Trust, UK.

The Basics Series

The Basics is a highly successful series of accessible guidebooks which provide an overview of the fundamental principles of a subject area in a jargon-free and undaunting format.

Intended for students approaching a subject for the first time, the books both introduce the essentials of a subject and provide an ideal springboard for further study. With over 50 titles spanning subjects from artificial intelligence (AI) to women's studies, *The Basics* are an ideal starting point for students seeking to understand a subject area.

Each text comes with recommendations for further study and gradually introduces the complexities and nuances within a subject.

For a full list of titles in this series, please visit
www.routledge.com/The-Basics/book-series/B

EATING DISORDERS

THE BASICS

**Dr Elizabeth McNaught,
Professor Janet Treasure, and Jess Griffiths**

Routledge
Taylor & Francis Group

NEW YORK AND LONDON

Designed cover image: © Getty Images

First published 2024
by Routledge
605 Third Avenue, New York, NY 10158

and by Routledge
4 Park Square, Milton Park, Abingdon, Oxon, OX14 4RN

Routledge is an imprint of the Taylor & Francis Group, an informa business

© 2024 Dr Elizabeth McNaught, Professor Janet Treasure, and Jess Griffiths

Library of Congress Cataloging-in-Publication Data
Names: McNaught, Elizabeth, author. | Treasure, Janet, author. |
Griffiths, Jess, author.
Title: Eating disorders: the basics / Dr. Elizabeth McNaught,
Professor Janet Treasure, and Jess Griffiths.
Description: New York, NY : Routledge, 2024. | Includes bibliographical
references and index. | Identifiers: LCCN 2023030822 (print) |
LCCN 2023030823 (ebook) | ISBN 9781032379593 (hbk) |
ISBN 9781032379579 (pbk) | ISBN 9781003342762 (ebk)
Subjects: LCSH: Eating disorders.
Classification: LCC RC552.E18 M417 2024 (print) |
LCC RC552.E18 (ebook) | DDC 616.85/26--dc23/eng/20220330
LC record available at https://lccn.loc.gov/2023030822
LC ebook record available at https://lccn.loc.gov/2023030823

ISBN: 978-1-032-37959-3 (hbk)
ISBN: 978-1-032-37957-9 (pbk)
ISBN: 978-1-003-34276-2 (ebk)

DOI: 10.4324/9781003342762

Typeset in Bembo Std
by KnowledgeWorks Global Ltd.

CONTENTS

ACKNOWLEDGEMENTS

Marina, Chris Avenell, Suzanne Baker, Dave Chawner, Meera Chohan, Stacey Dooley, Adam Fare, F.E.A.S.T. – www.feast-ed. org/, Florence Greenwood, Dave Griffiths, Laura Hanton, Anjali Heer, Anya Heneghan, Anny Johnson – Anny of The Fat.Ugly Blog, Professor Tim Kendall, Cara Lisette, Sharon Miklosova – the BED post blog, Sarah Miller, Stephen Parish, Naomi Parnell, Nick Pollard – co-founder of Family Mental Wealth, Sophie Reindorp, Rochelle Rouse, Jess Sharman, Nicky Smith, Chelsea Spencer, Kirsty Stapledon, Christina Taylor.

ABOUT THE AUTHORS

Dr Elizabeth McNaught is a GP with a special interest in mental health. She is the co-founder and medical director of Family Mental Wealth (a government-funded social enterprise developing digital tools to facilitate family-based self-help for mental health and wellbeing). She is the author of *Life Hurts: A Doctor's Personal Journey Through Anorexia* and co-editor, with Prof Janet Treasure and Nick Pollard, of *Eating Disorders* (an Oxford Specialist Handbook in Psychiatry).

Professor Janet Treasure is a professor at King's College London and a consultant psychiatrist at the South London and Maudsley NHS Foundation Trust. A key focus of her research has been working with people with lived experience of an eating disorder (patients and carers) to co-design, co-develop and co-deliver new treatments with a particular focus on people with a severe enduring illness or comorbidities such as diabetes. Janet has had a particular interest in the biological, psychological, and social risk and maintaining factors, and how these may be targeted in treatment. She has been involved in the training of medical practitioners, psychologists, and clinical academics, as well as editing seven academic texts on eating disorders and co-authoring three self-help books with people with lived experience.

Jess Griffiths is a therapist specialising in eating disorders and works as the national co-lead for FREED (First Episode Rapid Early Intervention for Eating Disorders) at the South London and

Maudsley NHS Foundation Trust. Jess co-chairs the Parliamentary and Health Service Ombudsman's delivery group at NHS England that was formed after the publication of *Ignoring the Alarms – How NHS Eating Disorder Services are Failing Patients*. Jess is passionate about training and works alongside the Maudsley, delivering training for adult eating disorder services, therapists, and health care professionals.

INTRODUCTION
Jess Griffiths

CONTEXT

Eating disorders affect an estimated 1.25 million people in the UK (Beat, 2017). They are complex mental illnesses that can present in many different ways – anyone can be affected by them.

Within this book, we will attempt to outline the main eating disorders, namely anorexia nervosa, bulimia nervosa, binge eating disorder, other specified feeding or eating disorder, pica, rumination disorder and avoidant restrictive food intake disorder.

The book has been written as part of the Routledge Basics series to offer information about eating disorders that is accessible for all. The content is suitable for school and health care professionals, students and family members. The authors come with a wide range of experience to guide you through the journey from identification, treatment, and to recovery. Within the chapters, you will hear the stories of people who have experienced eating disorders, as well as those who have supported people through them. Our hope is that readers of the book will feel equipped, inspired, and more confident to support people experiencing eating disorders.

MEET THE AUTHORS

Elizabeth McNaught is a GP and co-founder and medical director of Family Mental Wealth. She is the author of *Life Hurts: A Doctor's Personal Journey Through Anorexia* and co-author of *Eating Disorders* (an Oxford Specialist Handbook in Psychiatry).

DOI: 10.4324/9781003342762-1

Professor Janet Treasure is a professor at King's College London and a consultant psychiatrist at the South London and Maudsley NHS Foundation Trust. She has edited seven academic texts on eating disorders and co-authored three self-help books.

Jess is a therapist specialising in eating disorders, and works as the national co-lead for FREED (First Episode Rapid Early Intervention for Eating Disorders) at the South London and Maudsley NHS Foundation Trust. She has lived experience of an eating disorder and is fully recovered.

We start the book in Chapter 2, with an overview of eating disorders and will outline the research that explores the causes, vulnerabilities and triggers to eating disorders. The diagnostic criteria for eating disorders are explained and the co-morbid conditions that often present alongside are outlined. There is also an introduction to the National Institute for Clinical Excellence (NICE, 2017) guidelines on the assessment and evidence-based treatment of eating disorders.

Our typical image of a person who has an eating disorder might be of a white, middle-class, adolescent girl, but the reality is that anyone of any age, ethnic background, gender, or class can be impacted by them. Chapter 3 discusses diverse presentations of eating disorders and how people from underrepresented groups may struggle to reach out for support and the possible reasons for this.

Chapters 4–10 outline each of the named eating disorders, the risk factors for their development, how a health care professional may assess and diagnose them, and the brief outline of the evidence-based treatments.

It's not about food! If I'd learned early on that food was numbing what I was feeling and that I needed to learn strategies to cope with difficult feelings that weren't self-medicating, I could have started that much earlier.

Christina Taylor, lived experience of anorexia nervosa

Eating disorders are treatable illnesses that often require support from a multidisciplinary team (MDT). Treatment for more serious physical complications around eating disorders often requires medical and dietetics input and intervention. Chapter 11 outlines the most up-to-date evidence-based treatment for eating disorders according to the NICE (2017) guidelines.

> Over the next year I was fortunate enough to receive a range of treatments, seeing a psychotherapist and occupational therapist, a psychiatrist and a dietician. Instead of going to lectures and club nights, I was going to doctor appointments and therapy sessions. Instead of revising for exams, I was poring over meal plans. I wanted to get better, I wanted to get back to my life and get rid of the cruel eating disorder voice that plagued my every waking thought, but, like most people with anorexia, I did not want to gain weight. I was adamant that it wasn't necessary to recover, despite everything my treatment team were telling me.
>
> Laura Hanton – lived experience of anorexia nervosa

Family support is vital to the effective treatment of eating disorders. In Chapter 12, we outline the therapies that family are involved in and the skills that carers and supporters learn about to support loved ones through the illness.

> The first people who became aware were my amazing parents. They very quickly acknowledged that there was a problem and tried everything they could to get treatment and support for me.
>
> Adam Fare – lived experience of other specified feeding eating disorder

Eating disorders are treatable illnesses that people fully recover from. In Chapter 13, you'll read the 'letters of hope' and the advice that is offered from the perspective of lived experience and how individuals reached a place of recovery and a life free from an eating disorder.

Never, ever give up hope, hold the hope for your loved one, when they are not able to hold it for themselves. Recovery is possible at any age and stage.

Suzanne Baker – lived experience of caring for two daughters with anorexia nervosa

If I could go back in time and give advice to the younger me, or to someone else in a similar position, it would be this ... don't give up. Keep fighting, and let your loved ones fight for you as well. The hardest step is to realise you're not an island and cannot do it all yourself. But most of all, find out who you really are. Not who others think you are, not what your school grades suggest you should do in the future. Find what you want to do, what you love – and pursue that. The happiest I have ever been is doing things I love and supporting others. Find your passion, and you will be able to thrive.

Adam Fare – lived experience of other specified feeding or eating disorder

Try and think about who you are, as a whole person, and what's important to you. Find your reasons to recover, whatever they may be. I would also say to reach out for support. Eating disorders can be such a lonely, dark place, but you don't have to do it alone. There is help out there. And reaching out doesn't always mean talking – I started my writing a letter to my stepmum! So, there are ways to get your voice heard – find what works for you.

Jess Sharman – lived experience of other specified feeding or eating disorder

The main message we want to send is that full recovery is possible. Although it was sometimes hard, we always maintained an atmosphere where communication without anger, frustration or judgement was possible. Patience and listening with loving understanding were the keys to us coming through to the other side of eating disorders.

David Griffiths – lived experience of caring for his wife with anorexia nervosa and bulimia nervosa

REFERENCES

Beat. (2017). *Delaying for years, denied for months*. Beat: London. https://beat. contentfiles.net/media/documents/delaying-for-years-denied-for-months.pdf.

National Institute for Health and Care Excellence. (2017). *Eating disorders: recognition and treatment*. NICE guideline [NG69]. London: NICE. www. nice.org.uk/guidance/ng69/chapter/Recommendations.

2

EATING DISORDERS OVERVIEW
Professor Janet Treasure

INTRODUCTION

The profile and prevalence of eating disorders has changed rapidly over the last 40 years since bulimia nervosa (BN) was described as a possible variant of anorexia nervosa (AN) in 1979. Since that time, various forms of binge spectrum disorders have emerged. Environmental factors such as changes in the food environment and the stigmatisation of obesity and valuation of leanness have contributed to the changing form and epidemiology of eating disorders. The belief that eating disorders only occur in privileged, white females has now been dismissed as a myth. It is now recognised that the population at risk of developing problems with eating are diverse in terms of various sociodemographic features such as age, gender, sexuality, and ethnicity (Burke et al., 2022). Eating disorders may be triggered by both general adversities or by specific traumas relating to eating and body image. The genetic vulnerabilities associated with eating disorders are an area of active investigation, although currently AN is the only form of eating disorder with a sample large enough to be informative. The changes in eating behaviour and the associated social and physical consequences can interrupt development and produce secondary effects that maintain the illness.

THE WHAT, HOW, AND WHY OF EATING DISORDERS

The form of eating disorders has diversified and increased since Sir William Gull (a UK physician) and Charles Lasegue (a French psychiatrist) first introduced the concept of AN to the medical community

DOI: 10.4324/9781003342762-2

in the 19th century. The next milestone was the description of BN, initially considered to be "an ominous variant of anorexia nervosa" (Russell, 1979). This was characterised by recurrent, compulsive episodes of loss of control (binge) eating followed by extreme compensatory behaviours such as purging, often accompanied by shame.

> While many components of eating disorders are insidious, creeping on you slowly, convincing you are in control rather than the eating disorder, the nature of bulimia – bingeing and purging – meant that pretty quickly I knew a line had been crossed.
>
> Bulimia can often feel like a failed or lesser eating disorder, so challenging this in myself and trying to recognise I deserve help and that this isn't my fault ... is definitely a work in progress.
>
> Marina

In the 21st century, the most common forms of eating disorders are binge eating disorder (BED), and other variants of disordered eating subsumed under the diagnostic label of other specified feeding or eating disorders (OSFED). Also, avoidant restrictive food intake disorder (ARFID), rumination disorder and pica, which were previously within the category of childhood disorders of eating, have been added to the wider category of eating disorders in both the American and the World Health Organization diagnostic manuals (DSM-5, American Psychiatric Association, 2013; ICD-11, World Health Organization, 2022). Some of the eating disorder variants differ by gender (bigorexia/muscle dysmorphic disorder tend to occur more commonly in men) or with comorbidity, such as in people with Type 1 diabetes (sometimes labelled as diabulimia). Some of these are outlined in Table 2.1.

TYPE 1 DIABETES WITH DISORDERED EATING (T1DE)

People with Type 1 diabetes are two to three times more likely to have an eating disorder. This form of eating disorder is sometimes also known as diabulimia, because one aspect of this eating disorder variant is to omit or reduce their insulin requirement as a means of purging. In addition, a range of other problems with diabetes management may also be manifest. Many diabetes services have developed the expertise to manage this form of complexity.

Table 2.1   Potential emerging variant forms of eating disorders

Disorder	Symptoms
Reverse anorexia, bigorexia, muscle dysmorphic disorder	Drive for muscularity, leanness and tone rather than thinness (often seen in men). Associated with the use of medications or nutritional supplements to "bulk up".
Type 1 diabetes with disordered eating (T1DE), diabulimia	Reduction in insulin used as a means of weight loss or to manage emotions.
Food addiction	Gradually the size and frequency of eating, and overconsumption, increases. Highly processed food is incriminated.
Orthorexia	Food choice limited to "clean" or "healthy" food, at a cost to wellbeing.

By my late 20s, I was in full-scale diabetes burnout – a state of mental and emotional overwhelm from managing diabetes 24/7. I neglected my diabetes care, skipped insulin, and stopped caring about my physical and mental health.

I began managing my glucose levels by restricting carbs instead of using insulin. Diabetes self-care felt overwhelming, and I wanted to avoid it at all costs. This short-term relief of avoidance led to many hospital admissions from life-threatening diabetic ketoacidosis. My body couldn't sustain the restriction of carbs and insulin, and my attitude towards food became unhealthily obsessive.

The only option was an inpatient admission to an eating disorder unit ... [There] was a lot of work to be done around safely reintroducing insulin, weight restoration while managing carbohydrate counting and the mental health challenges that brings. Recovery took much longer than I anticipated, but I'm safely managing my diabetes independently now, and have learned coping strategies for when diabetes feels relentless and burnout hits.

Every day I'm faced with the temptation to return to eating disorder behaviours simply because type 1 diabetes requires counting carbs and responding to numbers multiple times a day. Self-compassion is the only thing that keeps me from falling off this tightrope ... self-compassion has taught me that those numbers don't define me. Whether that be blood sugar, carbs, insulin, or weight, numbers are data, not a grade or a measure of my worth.

Nay Parnell

FOOD ADDICTION

Research into the neuroscience of eating disorders has led to the introduction of the concept of food addiction. There is an obvious overlap with binge eating disorders, but the concept remains controversial.

THE EPIDEMIOLOGY OF EATING DISORDERS

As new forms of eating disorders are described, the reported figures for the incidence and prevalence change. Thus, after Gerald Russell named and described BN in 1979, an increase in the number of cases of BN presenting to primary care in the UK followed (Currin et al., 2004; Micali et al., 2013). Similarly, an increase in binge eating disorders and other forms of eating disorders followed the diagnostic changes made in DSM-5 (*Diagnostic and Statistical Manual of Mental Disorders*; American Psychiatric Association, 2913). However, the exact prevalence and incidence rates of eating disorders are uncertain, as many people do not recognise their symptoms as part of an illness and/or do not present for treatment.

> While I had struggled with food and my body image for as long as I could remember, anorexia took hold swiftly and my life transformed within a few short months. I became isolated, obsessive, and terrified of any and all situations involving food. Yet I refused to believe I had an eating disorder. I didn't think I was ill enough, or thin enough, to have anorexia. I believed that I was fine and could stop these weird habits and behaviours whenever I wanted to. I ignored the concern in my friends' faces and the fear in my sister's eyes and the worry in my mum's words; I thought they were all just overreacting.
>
> Laura Hanton

Approximately 10 per cent of the female population (and a lower prevalence in males) have some form of eating disorder during their lifetime. For the most part, these are within the binge spectrum of disorders, whereas the lifetime prevalence of disorders associated with being underweight with restricted eating (AN and ARFID) is lower, at approximately 2 per cent.

All forms of eating disorder are often comorbid with other conditions. For example, over 20 per cent of people with AN are comorbid with obsessive compulsive disorder (OCD) and a smaller proportion may be comorbid with autism spectrum disorder (ASD). The traits associated with ASD, such as sensory sensitivity, perfectionism, comfort from following rules, problems with uncertainty and ambiguity, and social difficulties (victim of bullying or exclusion), often become entangled with the illness. In some cases, the two forms of neurodiversity – attention deficit hyperactivity disorder (ADHD) (which is more commonly seen in those with binge spectrum disorders) and ASD – coexist and can pull in different directions.

Another really difficult part has been managing these permanent issues, being autistic and ADHD, and having an eating disorder. Each one of these sorts of contradicts the other. My autism needs routine and hates change. My ADHD needs change and is very impulsive.

Adam Fare

THE ENVIRONMENTAL SETTING FOR THE DEVELOPMENT OF EATING DISORDER

The rapid changes in the form and prevalence of eating disorders in the last 50 years suggests that environmental factors play a role. Changes in the food environment that have been implicated include food poverty, ultra-processed foods, and a reduction in shared, home-produced meals. Concurrently, with these changes in the food environment, social media has disseminated the value of leanness and the stigmatisation of larger bodies. These factors have also been implicated in the parallel increase of obesity. The shared and differing risk factors between obesity and eating disorders has made prevention efforts complex.

I can recall struggling with my body image from around age 7. I grew up in a household where diets and bodies were talked about frequently, and I started to become interested in weighing myself by Year 6, though didn't at that time understand too much about what those numbers meant. I remember looking through Weight Watchers paraphernalia and having the "red" [bad] food scarred into my brain, quickly learning that red foods meant weight gain, and weight gain was bad. It was around this age that I began comparing myself to other children, always measuring my thighs in my gymnastics leotard to the girls around me or scanning holiday Polaroids to see if I looked bigger in my swimming costume than the other children by the pool.

Cara Lisette

COVID: A NATURAL EXPERIMENT

COVID-19 was associated with a marked increase in the presentation of eating disorders. There was an increase in the presentation and admission of cases of severe AN, for instance (Devoe et al., 2023). Some of the environmental changes during lockdown mapped onto the risks known to be associated with AN. For example, the key role of isolation echoes a quote from a doctor with the lived experience of AN: "I was recently asked to sum up my experience of anorexia nervosa in one sentence – actually, I can do it in just one word – isolation" (McKnight et al., 2009).

Other potential contributing factors include increased screen time, leading to a higher exposure to social media and an increase in "fat talk" with concerns about weight gain, exemplified by the "quarantine 15" (reports of 15lb/7kg weight gain during lockdown), and weight stigma (concerns about a higher mortality risk from COVID-19 in intensive care amongst those with larger bodies). Also, the generalised sense of threat and uncertainty produced a high-risk environment for those with an anxious disposition.

PREDISPOSING, PRECIPITATING, AND PERPETUATING FACTORS

Environmental exposures interact with more personal forms of vulnerabilities such as genetic and developmental factors to increase the risk of developing an eating disorder. The risks for developing an eating disorder can be considered within the headings of predisposing factors (including genetic, environmental, and developmental factors), precipitating factors (those environmental and developmental factors that may have triggered the problem), and perpetuating factors (those that may have developed as secondary consequences of the illness and/or lead to the problem being maintained), as shown in Table 2.2 for AN and Table 2.3 for binge spectrum disorders.

GENETIC RISK FACTORS

Early twin and family studies gave the first hint that genetic factors were involved. Further research into the genetic aspects of eating disorders has shown, using genome wide association studies, that

Table 2.2 The predisposing, precipitating, and perpetuating factors for AN

	Predisposing	Precipitating	Perpetuating
Genetic	• Insulin sensitivity • Low lipids • Low body mass index (BMI) • Obsessive compulsive and anxiety traits		• Weak homeostatic forces following negative energy balance • Eating disorder aligns with traits of anxiety, perfectionism, rigidity and fear of uncertainty
Environment	• Adversity • Concerns about shape and weight	• Negative energy balance: decreased intake and/ or increased expenditure • Stress	• Weight stigma and diet culture
Development		• Puberty • Menopause	

Table 2.3 The predisposing, precipitating, and perpetuating factors for binge spectrum disorder

	Predisposing	Precipitating	Perpetuating
Genetic	• Insulin resistance • High lipids • High BMI • ADHD and addiction traits		• Strong homeostatic forces following negative energy balance

Environment:	• Trauma
	• Social alienation and minority status due to:
	  • Race
	  • Gender
	  • Sexuality
	  • Poverty
	  • Adversity
	  • Concerns about shape and weight
	  • Family history of addiction
		• Negative energy balance: decreased intake and/ or increased expenditure
		• Stress
			• Weight stigma and diet culture
			• Difficulties in emotional regulation, possibly related to childhood adversity

Development:		• Puberty	

AN is associated with a genetic profile linked to both the brain and body. Thus, there are associations in the profile of AN, and metabolic factors such as low BMI, insulin sensitivity and variations in the lipid profile, with various psychiatric disorders, in particular OCD (Watson et al., 2019). AN could therefore be classified as a form of psychosomatic disorder.

> Research is currently under way to collect cohorts of patients with the other forms of eating disorders large enough to be informative. Early findings suggest that the genetic profile of AN and binge spectrum disorders diverge in terms of metabolic risk factors.

PREDISPOSING AND TRIGGERING ENVIRONMENTAL EVENTS

Specific environmental events during development – for example, trauma and forms of adversity such as food poverty, discrimination, and alienation due to race, gender, or sexuality – are associated with a higher risk, particularly for binge spectrum disorders (Solmi et al., 2015). These minoritised vulnerabilities are less commonly seen in AN.

Personal stories suggest that in many cases the triggers for AN may be non-specific adversities. However, it is thought that they gain momentum from the background predisposition (e.g., perfectionistic traits) and the perpetuating factors (such as starvation-related changes that may follow).

> I enjoyed what I was doing! That's an uncomfortable truth, right?! I'm not glorifying, promoting, or encouraging disordered behaviour, but it's something that is important to be honest about. I got a kick out of it. Or at least I had originally. However, that kick got harder and harder to get. I had to work more and more to get any enjoyment out of it. The balance tipped from enjoyment to compulsion.
>
> Dave Chawner

> The eating disorder reeled me in with a false sense of security and power. However, I quickly realised I was far from in control, and my behaviours soon became addictive and impulsive.
>
> Kirsty Stapledon

The biological and social developmental changes associated with puberty may set the scene for the onset of an eating disorder, possibly through interacting with the risk factors described above. There is some evidence that menopausal changes may also contribute to risk. An episode of weight loss commonly (although not always), intentionally, caused by food restriction or negative energy balance (possibly associated with increased energy expenditure due to the pubertal growth spurt and/or increased exercise), often precedes the development of an eating disorder.

WHAT PERPETUATES AN EATING DISORDER?

Eating disorders, particularly AN, often run a protracted course. For example, the average illness duration has been found to be seven years. One explanation for this is that the disorders may not lead to early help-seeking (Chapter 12) and may activate a wide range of physiological, psychological, and social maintaining factors.

Metabolic perpetuating factors

An unverified hypothesis is that the genetic metabolic variants associated with AN produce an atypical response to weight loss characterised by overactivity and restlessness. This increases weight loss, and the homeostatic mechanisms that are normally activated to restore weight have less power. This contrasts with the binge spectrum disorders, in which weight loss is associated with dysphoria and increased hunger and the appetite drive is strongly increased, leading to binge eating. Sometimes there is an initial overshoot of weight restoration which perpetuates the drive to diet – that is, weight/appetite might remain higher for a time, but should eventually come back to normal.

Another unproven hypothesis to account for binge spectrum disorders is that wide fluxes in glucose due to insulin resistance and bingeing behaviour on foods, which produces rapid fluxes in blood sugar, trigger an addictive process that fuels the persisting pattern of fasting and binge eating (Treasure et al., 2015).

The continuing unregulated weight loss associated with AN leads to malnutrition. Metabolically active organs are particularly compromised. For example, the brain, which requires 300–500 kcal per day to function, compensates by reducing brain growth factors and adolescents lose 6 per cent of their brain structure in the early phase of the illness (Walton et al., 2022). Brain maturation changes that occur during adolescence, such as synaptic pruning, are paused. This adaptation of the brain to starvation leads to secondary problems, including autistic-like features of reduced social expressivity and responsivity. Memory and visuospatial learning are also impacted (Stedal et al., 2021).

Consider this quotation from a qualitative study, which illustrates how memory function during the illness was disrupted: "it's so weird, I feel like I didn't realise like how much of it I just do not recall until having to, like actively think about it, it's really odd" (Keeler et al., 2022).

These secondary effects directly on the brain, or indirectly through the regression of reproductive development during the pubertal process, interfere with the establishment of a mature and secure adult identity (Treasure et al., 2020). They also explain why early reversal of symptoms leads to a better outcome.

> Weight restoration is one small part of recovery, but it makes everything else so much easier. You can't do much while your body and brain are in starvation and thinking of nothing but food. I could barely hold a conversation, let alone engage in therapy. It was only once I was a healthier weight, and eating regularly, that the psychological work started to make sense. I began to understand the underlying reasons for my eating disorder and the things that were keeping it alive, which in turn meant I could make the changes needed to start building my life back up.
>
> Laura Hanton

Personality factors

Some of the consequences of an eating disorder become valued through their interaction with predisposing traits such as perfectionism, fear of uncertainty, and anxiety. Professor Walter Kaye, an eminent academic in the field, suggests that good traits have been turned to the bad in

Table 2.4   How strong personality factors in AN can cause harm when applied to the eating disorder

Good outcome	Good goal	Trait	Bad goal	Bad outcome
Balanced life goals between body and mind	Optimising goals within the constraints of time, energy, and value	Perfectionism	Extreme weight control	The brain centres that control eating through metabolic homeostatic factors, and those that use cognitive methods such as will power, are in conflict
A strong moral compass	A good enough citizen	Sensitivity to social censure	Extreme control over body	A follower of fashion
A sensitive, nurturing environment	A safety net allowing just enough risk	Anxiety	A risk-free environment	Stunted growth

AN (see Table 2.4 for examples of this). For example, the traits of anxiety, which include a fear of uncertainty and perfectionism (which can benefit social order), also align with eating disorder rules. Following these rules can be a comfort for people who find uncertainty difficult. Furthermore, the goal of weight loss is strongly reinforced in people with perfectionistic traits. Also, the challenges and uncertainty associated with social milestones can be avoided because of the regression of development. Thus, these traits allow eating disorder habits to become entrenched. Eating disorder values displace the emerging identity, making recovery and future thinking difficult to imagine.

Neurobehavioural traits such as a high appetite drive are common in binge spectrum conditions. These traits may have had survival advantages in environmental settings, such as food insecurity. Nevertheless, these same traits may have evolved because they may facilitate social functioning within the tribe.

SOCIAL AND INTERPERSONAL MAINTAINING FACTORS

The overt features of starvation elicit a profound social response from others. (These are discussed more fully in Chapter 12.) Starvation and food refusal can produce a mixture of emotions, such as anxiety and/or frustration, which in turn leads to overprotection and accommodation to the eating disorder or criticism and withdrawal. These diverse reactions may fragment the family or social network, isolating the individual within the disorder and allowing the symptoms to be maintained.

The social reaction to binge spectrum disorder can also include anxiety, but also disgust, anger, and shame. These, and the secretive nature of these behaviours, can also serve to isolate the individual, which in turn leads to anxiety and low mood, which themselves trigger emotional overeating.

COGNITIVE INTERPERSONAL MODELS OF EATING DISORDER

Various models of treatment have been developed to target predisposing risk factors from the genetic, social, developmental, and environmental domains and the biological, psychological, and social factors that serve to maintain the disorder discussed above.

TREATMENT

> As time passed and the grips of the eating disorder tightened, I began to realise that the values and goals of the eating disorder did not align with my personal values. I started to understand that to have improved quality of life and accomplish any of my future aspirations, I needed to make a change.
>
> Kirsty Stapledon

Psychological, social (family), and inpatient (behavioural) treatments have all been used for the treatment of AN (see Chapter 11). For example, exposure strategies are used to counter avoidance and anxiety about food- and/or body-shape-related behaviours. Behavioural experiments are introduced to moderate extreme strategies of cognitive or emotional regulation. Skills training for supporters facilitates the development of a strong support network (Chapter 12).

A variety of factors can lead to treatment resistance. For example, there may be important comorbidities associated with AN — such as OCD, ASD, and depression — which may need a specific treatment focus. A specific pathway for people with autistic spectrum traits has been developed (Tchanturia et al., 2020). Also, feasibility trials of treatments for resistant depression (brain stimulation or drugs targeting novel receptors) are in the early stages of investigation (Karaszewska et al., 2022; Ledwos et al., 2023).

Binge spectrum disorders may be comorbid with diabetes, ADHD, trauma, and addictions. A form of treatment tailored for people with T1DE has been developed and tested (Broadley et al., 2020; Harrison et al., 2022). Similarly, protocols for the treatment of trauma associated with eating disorders are being tested (Trottier et al., 2022).

The course of illness can be bumpy, particularly for binge spectrum disorders.

> My relapse knocked me back a bit. I lost a certain level of hope and my level of self-belief and confidence plummeted. Again, due to continued family support, a nurturing home environment, and through taking very small steps outside of my comfort zone, I was able to slowly pick myself back up.
>
> Kirsty Stapledon

CONCLUSION

Eating disorders are conditions with both psychological and somatic underpinnings. A genetic predisposition may interact with social, developmental, and environmental factors to set the scene for the problem to begin. The disordered eating behaviours can allow the problems to be maintained, especially if there are additional forms of comorbidity. The symptoms impact on all life domains. It is possible that many of the environmental risk factors can be targeted using prevention strategies including reducing weight stigma, social censure, and food poverty. A detailed lifetime history, as part of a full formulation tailored to the specific problems and personalised to the stage and/or severity, can be a helpful start to treatment. Cognitive interpersonal models including various risk and maintaining factors form a template on which to build models for prevention and/or treatment.

SUMMARY

- The diagnostic definitions within the category of eating disorders have expanded following the addition of bulimia nervosa (BN) to anorexia nervosa (AN) in 1979.

- The ICD-11 and DSM-5 now have the following categories: anorexia nervosa, bulimia nervosa, binge eating disorder, avoidant restrictive food intake disorder (ARFID), rumination disorder, pica, other specified feeding and eating disorders (OSFED).
- Potential new diagnostic categories include type 1 diabetes with disordered eating (T1DE) and orthorexia nervosa.
- One in every six females and one in twenty males develop an eating disorder (Santamauro et al., 2021).
- The COVID-19 pandemic was associated with a large increase in eating disorders.
- AN is associated with a genetic profile linked to insulin sensitivity and low BMI.
- Early work suggests that binge spectrum disorders are associated with a genetic profile linked to insulin resistance and a high BMI.
- AN is associated with a genetic profile like that for obsessive compulsive disorders, whereas binge spectrum disorder shares a profile with ADHD and addictions.
- Starvation interrupts development and produces changes in the body and brain that can maintain an eating disorder.
- The psychological traits of anxiety, perfectionism, and a fear of uncertainty contribute to the perpetuation of AN.
- Problems with emotional regulation and impulsivity contribute to the perpetuation of binge spectrum disorders.
- Social factors such as overprotection or accommodation can allow AN to persist. Therefore, skills training of supporters improves outcomes.

REFERENCES

American Psychiatric Association. (2013). *Diagnostic and statistical manual of mental disorders: DSM-5*, 5th edition. Washington, DC: American Psychiatric Association.

Broadley, M. M., Zaremba, N., Andrew, B., Ismail, K., Treasure, J., White, M. J., & Stadler, M. (2020). 25 years of psychological research investigating disordered eating in people with diabetes: what have we learnt? *Diabetic Medicine*, 37(3), 401–408.

Burke, N. L., Hazzard, V. M., Schaefer, L. M., Simone, M., O'Flynn, J. L., & Rodgers, R. F. (2022). Socioeconomic status and eating disorder prevalence: at the intersections of gender identity, sexual orientation, and race/ethnicity. *Psychological Medicine*, 53(9), 1–11.

Currin, L., Schmidt, U., Treasure, J., & Jick, H. (2005). Time trends in eating disorder incidence. *British Journal of Psychiatry*, 186(2), 132–135.

Devoe, D. J., Han, A., Anderson, A., Katzman, D. K., Patten, S. B., Soumbasis, A., … & Dimitropoulos, G. (2023). The impact of the COVID-19 pandemic on eating disorders: a systematic review. *International Journal of Eating Disorders*, 56(1), 5–25.

Harrison, A., Zaremba, N., Brown, J., Allan, J., Konstantara, E., Hopkins, D., ... & Stadler, M. (2021). A cognitive behavioural model of the bidirectional relationship between disordered eating and diabetes self-care in people with type 1 diabetes mellitus. *Diabetic Medicine*, 38(7), e14578.

Karaszewska, D., Cleintuar, P., Oudijn, M., Lok, A., van Elburg, A., Denys, D., & Mocking, R. (2022). Efficacy and safety of deep brain stimulation for treatment-refractory anorexia nervosa: a systematic review and meta-analysis. *Translational Psychiatry*, 12(1), 333.

Keeler, J. L., Konyn, C. Y., Treasure, J., Cardi, V., Himmerich, H., Tchanturia, K., & Mycroft, H. (2022). "Your mind doesn't have room for anything else": a qualitative study of perceptions of cognitive functioning during and after recovery from anorexia nervosa. *Journal of Eating Disorders*, 10(1), 1–18.

Ledwos, N., Rodas, J. D., Husain, M. I., Feusner, J. D., & Castle, D. J. (2023). Therapeutic uses of psychedelics for eating disorders and body dysmorphic disorder. *Journal of Psychopharmacology*, 37(1), 3–13.

McKnight, R., & Boughton, N. (2009). A patient's journey Anorexia nervosa. *British Medical Journal*, 339.

Micali, N., Hagberg, K. W., Petersen, I., & Treasure, J. L. (2013). The incidence of eating disorders in the UK in 2000–2009: findings from the General Practice Research Database. *BMJ Open*, 3(5), e002646.

Russell, G. (1979). Bulimia nervosa: an ominous variant of anorexia nervosa. *Psychological Medicine*, 9(3), 429–448.

Solmi, F., Hotopf, M., Hatch, S. L., Treasure, J., & Micali, N. (2016). Eating disorders in a multi-ethnic inner-city UK sample: prevalence, comorbidity and service use. *Social Psychiatry and Psychiatric Epidemiology*, 51, 369–381.

Stedal, K., Broomfield, C., Hay, P., Touyz, S., & Scherer, R. (2021). Neuropsychological functioning in adult anorexia nervosa: a meta-analysis. *Neuroscience & Biobehavioral Reviews*, 130, 214–226.

Tchanturia, K., Smith, K., Glennon, D., & Burhouse, A. (2020). Towards an improved understanding of the anorexia nervosa and autism spectrum comorbidity: PEACE pathway implementation. *Frontiers in Psychiatry*, 11, 640.

Treasure, J., Kan, C., Stephenson, L., Warren, E., Smith, E., Heller, S., & Ismail, K. (2015). Developing a theoretical maintenance model for disordered eating in Type 1 diabetes. *Diabetic Medicine*, 32(12), 1541–1545.

Treasure, J., Willmott, D., Ambwani, S., Cardi, V., Clark Bryan, D., Rowlands, K., & Schmidt, U. (2020). Cognitive interpersonal model for anorexia nervosa revisited: The perpetuating factors that contribute to the development of the severe and enduring illness. *Journal of Clinical Medicine*, 9(3), 630.

Trottier, K., Monson, C. M., Wonderlich, S. A., & Crosby, R. D. (2022). Results of the first randomized controlled trial of integrated cognitive-behavioral therapy for eating disorders and posttraumatic stress disorder. *Psychological Medicine*, 52(3), 587–596.

Walton, E., Bernardoni, F., Batury, V. L., Bahnsen, K., Larivière, S., Abbate-Daga, G., ... & Ehrlich, S. (2022). Brain structure in acutely underweight and partially weight-restored individuals with anorexia nervosa: a coordinated analysis by the ENIGMA Eating Disorders Working Group. *Biological Psychiatry*, 92(9), 730–738.

Watson, H. J., Yilmaz, Z., Thornton, L. M., Hübel, C., Coleman, J. R., Gaspar, H.A., ... & Seitz, J. (2019). Genome-wide association study identifies eight risk loci and implicates metabo-psychiatric origins for anorexia nervosa. *Nature Genetics*, 51(8), 1207–1214.

World Health Organization. (2022). *ICD-11: international classification of diseases*, 11th revision. https://icd.who.int/

3

DIVERSITY IN EATING DISORDERS

Jess Griffiths

INTRODUCTION

The predominant image for people experiencing eating disorders can often be centred around skinny, white, affluent girls (SWAG). This stereotype is driven by the media, including news reports, films, and documentaries.

Other groups in society, such as men, racial minorities, transgender individuals, and those from socioeconomically disadvantaged backgrounds, can remain in our communities but struggle with their eating disorder, left untreated for years (Beat, 2017).

EATING DISORDERS IN BLACK, ASIAN AND MINORITY ETHNIC (BAME) COMMUNITIES

During 2017–2018, there was a steeper increase in all admissions to hospital for eating disorders. The group that showed the sharpest increase in admissions were from ethnic minority backgrounds (Guardian, 2020).

Studies exploring the treatment of eating disorders amongst ethnic minorities in Western settings found that:

- Treatment seeking and treatment receiving is poor amongst BAME groups when compared to Caucasians.
- There was less awareness amongst primary and secondary services when diagnosing eating disorders and making appropriate referrals to specialist eating disorder services.

DOI: 10.4324/9781003342762-3

- People from BAME communities exhibiting symptoms of eating disorders were less likely to be referred to specialist eating disorder services.

(Sinha and Warfa, 2013)

The impact of views around the "thin ideal" and eating disorder prevalence in ethnic minorities is problematic for two reasons. First is the assumption that internalisation of the thin ideal is present for all eating disorder sufferers and the only driving factor for onset. Second is the assumption that this thin ideal is irrelevant in the minority populations. While some studies suggest it is less present, others indicate similar or higher levels of body dissatisfaction and suggest that, for black people highly acculturated to white culture, drive for thinness is higher (Fernandes et al., 2010).

Factors affecting help-seeking for BAME populations

Treatment for eating disorders is not always designed to take into consideration the impact of cultural differences on symptoms – individuals may understandably feel less safe in bringing these aspects of their illness to treatment spaces in fear of a clinician's lack of understanding. This is further compounded by a lack of black clinicians, including dietitians within the field of eating disorders, with research suggesting black individuals feel more comfortable exploring these themes with clinicians who look like them.

Although the narrative around mental illness may be changing, within BAME communities it continues to be seen as a sign of personal weakness, and open communication regarding mental health is often avoided. Further, to this, the narrative of being a "strong black individual", which is upheld both within the black community itself and reinforced by mainstream media, is a further barrier to seeking support (Mantovani et al., 2017).

Some people from BAME communities might fear that the diagnosis does not apply to "people like them", often assuming that they don't "look like" people who get eating disorders.

Research suggests that there is a general lack of trust in the health care system amongst ethnic minority groups; the recent difference in COVID-19 vaccine uptake has shed light on this. Reasons for this may include previous unethical health care research in black populations, underrepresentation in research and trials, and negative experiences within a culturally insensitive system (Razai et al., 2021).

People from ethnic minorities who have experienced binge eating disorder and bulimia nervosa in larger bodies have expressed how their difficulties are minimised by health professionals. They may be told that their weight is normal in "their community". As a result, they are often given unhelpful messages to continue to lose weight or, worse, find themselves signposted to weight loss services.

We know that black individuals are disproportionately more likely to be from a lower socioeconomic background in this country. We also know the constraints around funding and eating disorder treatment, with more individuals having to consider private input. This highlights a further barrier to treatment access that will be exacerbated for those from ethnic minority backgrounds.

THE IMPACT OF RACISM ON EATING DISORDERS

A literature review published in 2021 suggested that racial teasing and discrimination were associated with disordered eating, disturbed body image, and depressive symptoms, primarily among females across multiple races. However, this highlighted the need for longitudinal studies to examine risk factors and the likelihood of eating disorder onset over time (Swann et al., 2021).

The experience of racial discrimination, is likely to impact mind–body connection, one's sense of self, and encourage a desire to conform to what is seen as the "norm" – all of which are often seen as precipitating/perpetuating factors in eating disorder development.

ADAPTING TREATMENT

A lot of work is being done to adapt therapy and treatment to minority population groups. It often takes an existing therapy as a starting point and then specifically adapts the language, values, metaphors, and techniques of that approach for a particular community. The adaptation and provision of this therapy is typically carried out by therapists who are members of that community. This ensures that the work is done by staff who have an inside knowledge of the language, values, and beliefs of that community.

Table 3.1   Percentage of diagnosed cases of eating disorders within gender identity and sexual orientation

Gender identity and sexual orientation	*Past year eating disorder diagnosis (%)*
Transgender individuals	15.82
Cisgender sexual minority men	2.06
Cisgender heterosexual men	0.55
Cisgender sexual minority women	3.52
Cisgender heterosexual women	1.85

Source: Diemer et al. (2015)

EATING DISORDERS IN THE LGBTQIA+ COMMUNITY

LGBTQIA+ adults and adolescents experience greater incidence of eating disorders and disordered eating behaviours than their heterosexual and cisgender counterparts (Table 3.1). Gay, bisexual, and transgender adults and adolescents were all at increased risk for eating disorders and disordered eating behaviours (Parker and Haringer, 2020).

Stereotypes such as "gay men are all muscle or thin" or "all individuals with anorexia are malnourished" can prevent people from seeking help. Other common barriers to treatment in the LGBTQIA+ community include a lack of culturally competent treatment (which addresses the complexity of unique sexuality and gender identity issues), lack of support from family and friends, and insufficient eating disorders education among LGBTQIA+ resource providers who are in a position to detect and intervene. Additionally, individuals in the LGBTQIA+ community experience unique risk factors that can cause them to face challenges when accessing treatment and support.

Risk factors when accessing treatment and support include:

- fear of rejection or experience of rejections by friends, family, and co-workers
- internalised negative messages/beliefs about oneself due to sexual orientation, non-normative gender expressions, or transgender identity

- experiences of violence and post-traumatic stress disorder (PTSD), which research shows sharply increases vulnerability to an eating disorder
- discrimination due to one's sexual orientation and/or gender identity
- being a victim of bullying due to one's sexual orientation and/or gender identity
- discordance between one's biological sex and gender identity
- inability to meet body image ideals within some LGBTQIA+ cultural contexts.

MEN AND EATING DISORDERS

The research around men who experience eating disorders is limited, with some studies estimating that around 25 per cent of cases are in men (Strother et al., 2012). This statistic is thought to be unrepresentative of the true number of men who have eating disorders.

According to Coopey and Johnson (2022), Strother et al.'s (2012) 25 per cent statistic could be non-representative because:

- Men are less likely to access support from their GP or seek support for a mental health issue.
- Men tend to present with less severe eating disorder symptoms, which is further exacerbated by health professionals being less accurate in recognising the symptoms of eating disorders.
- The social stigma that "men don't get eating disorders" means that health professionals may not investigate underlying eating disorder symptoms or perform further investigations needed for referral and diagnosis.
- Men with eating disorders can often present as striving to achieve a high muscle mass, which may be considered more "acceptable" and therefore impeding recognition from health professionals.
- Men can face pressures from society to "man up" and show less vulnerability, which could lead to more secrecy and shame about their eating disorder as well as being a barrier to treatment seeking.

COST OF LIVING CRISIS: FOOD POVERTY

Food insecurity is known to have a detrimental effect on mental health in general. It is likely to increase the risk of eating disorders, because people living in food poverty will have periods of restriction, high anxiety, and will be more likely to access cheap foods that might be high in calories, but less nutritious. Planning food shopping and meals more rigidly may also lead to more preoccupation around food and weight (Hazzard et al., 2020).

A personal reflection by a South Asian British woman recovering from anorexia:

From a young age, I've spent my life fighting anorexia nervosa, a serious psychological eating disorder. Even now I find it difficult to articulate how deadly this eating disorder is.

As a person from South Asian heritage, I've experienced first-hand the culture surrounding mental illness within my community. Rather than being seen as a real illness that warrants the same attention and level of care as physical ailments, eating disorders are frequently dismissed and denied. Sufferers are often stigmatised or silenced.

It is empowering to share my personal journey of survival and recovery. It refutes the stereotype of eating disorders affecting only young, affluent, white women. In reality, eating disorders affect people of all genders, ethnic groups, and ages. However, the experience for sufferers in a BAME (black, Asian and minority ethnic) community can be very different.

Mental illnesses remain a taboo topic in many BAME communities. Girls and women in the South Asian community face cultural and societal pressures, which can trigger or exacerbate disordered eating habits and behaviours. The female role carries an expectation to look good. Being light-skinned and thin is seen as necessary to be considered attractive. Furthermore, it's common in these communities to have family, friends, and relatives commenting on one's physical appearance.

Food plays a major role in South Asian culture, and this presents a challenge for anyone with an eating disorder. Gatherings of family and friends invariably focus on food, and there is a strong expectation to socialise and eat. Those who do not partake are seen as antisocial and their motives are misunderstood.

Eating disorders are often denied in my community. Family and friends can't grasp why you can't eat, and can exert overwhelming pressure. They assume you're not eating on purpose, to disobey or spite them. You're accused of not listening, of being dismissive of their wishes. They can't understand that you want to please them but there is something compelling you not to eat.

Even when mental illnesses are acknowledged, South Asian British people face unique barriers to seeking treatment. Even after diagnosis, sufferers may not want to visit the doctor, because they worry that the illness will be seen by their family as failure in parenting or upbringing. They fear it will adversely impact their education and they will fail to meet parental expectations.

In order to bring about positive change, we need to encourage a compassionate, understanding society where people feel able to talk about their illness. We need to ensure a greater understanding of the complexities of eating disorders and the associated mental health difficulties. Literature and research on eating disorders amongst the South Asian population in Britain are limited, resulting in ignorance and misunderstanding of the condition. We need to be creative in how we campaign to create better awareness of eating disorders within BAME communities – for example, forming inclusive support groups, finding BAME celebrities to share their experiences, and using local communication platforms to highlight the condition and available treatments. This could help to reduce health care inequalities and impress upon our community that eating disorders are real, complex, and devastating conditions with serious, sometimes fatal, consequences. The earlier treatment is sought, the better the sufferer's chance of recovery.

As a recovering person with anorexia, I've learned that quality of life is more important than how I look. Eating disorders are far from trivial and I'm compassionate towards myself during recovery, I don't judge my past battles and I don't feel ashamed of my struggles.

Eating disorders do not discriminate. Nor are they obvious in presentation. I'm passionate about creating the right support and understanding from our society, raising greater awareness, eradicating the stigma associated with mental health and to reduce misconceptions.

Meera Chohan

Adam's experience of treatment within eating disorder services

Over the past 14 years, I have tried to access help on more than 40 occasions. I have never received anything. This is despite being hospitalised age 18 due to the physical effects of my eating disorder, and the bowel issues which my eating disorder made a lot worse (to the extent I was incontinent, and any food caused absolute agony). After this hospital stay, I was assessed by services for six months, before they concluded that I did not fit into any funding bracket to be allowed treatment. So, once again, it was down to my family to pick up the pieces. They have never let me down and deserve so much more.

I am asexual. This means I do not have sexual attraction to other people. Right from when I first had contact with mental health services and medical professionals for assessments, I was asked about wanting a family, wanting a romantic relationship, and everything that "usually" involves. But it was almost like they were trying to push a version of happiness and recovery that I couldn't ever see in myself. What if I don't want what they think I want? I'd love to have someone by my side, someone I share mutual love with, and someone I can be my whole self with – but that doesn't have to involve the traditional "relationship goals".

I think it has just made things harder for me, but also made the likelihood of me getting any professional support even less, as it just adds another layer of "stuff" which current services sadly seem to run away from.

Along the way I have learned so much about myself, about my illnesses and disabilities, and about what really matters in life. Success is so much more than status, money, and what job you've got. It's about love, happiness, experiences, friendship, and – most importantly – identity.

Anny's experience of an initial appointment with her GP to discuss binge eating disorder

In February 2020 I was diagnosed with binge eating disorder at 37 years old. Although it was a relief to find out that my eating behaviours, and the distress I'd experienced because of it, weren't because I was an inherently bad person, it took a while for me to stop doubting that the diagnosis was real and true for me.

On the morning when I decided to go to my GP, I'd been sitting on the edge of my bed trying to gather the motivation to go to work. I didn't want to face getting dressed, or being around people. I wanted to hide under my duvet and pretend the world outside didn't exist.

I believed that, even after two years, I was still grieving the loss of my gran and all I needed was two weeks off work to get myself together. My idea of getting myself together and feeling better meant going to the gym, eating properly, and hopefully losing a bit of weight.

I went back and forth with reasons why I needed to be strong and go to work, but that particular morning I crumbled and had nothing left in me to keep pretending I was OK. My GP was a black woman, which made it easier to speak openly – I felt safe speaking to someone who looked like me. She was everything you'd expect a good GP to be; compassionate, kind, empathetic, and understanding, but most of all she was a good listener.

SUMMARY

- Eating disorders do not only affect young, white, middle-class females. They are prevalent in all communities, ages, and ethnicities.
- People from ethnic minority communities may struggle to reach out for help due to stigma and fear of institutionalised racism.
- Eating disorders are more common in the LGBTQIA+ community.
- Men struggle to seek support for their eating disorder, and current statistics may not be respresentative of the number of undiagnosed cases in the population.

REFERENCES

Beat. (2017). *Delaying for years, denied for months.* https://beat.contentfiles.net/media/documents/delaying-for-years-denied-for-months.pdf.

Coopey, E., & Johnson, G. (2022). "The male elephant in the room": a qualitative evidence synthesis exploring male experiences of eating disorders. *Journal of Eating Disorders*, 10(1). https://doi.org/10.1186/s40337-022-00614-w.

Diemer, E. W., Grant, J. D., Munn-Chernoff, M. A., Patterson, D. A., & Duncan, A. E. (2015). Gender identity, sexual orientation, and eating-related pathology in a national sample of college students. *Journal of Adolescent Health*, 57(2), 144–149.

Fernandes, N. H., Crow, S. J., Thuras, P., & Peterson, C. B. (2010). Characteristics of black treatment seekers for eating disorders. *International Journal of Eating Disorders*, 43(3), 282–285. doi:10.1002/eat.20684. PMID: 19343798; PMCID: PMC5546798.

Hazzard, V. M., Loth K. A., Hooper L., & Black Becker, C. (2020). Food insecurity and eating disorders: a review of emerging evidence. *Current Psychiatry Reports*, 22(12), 74. https://doi.org/10.1007/s11920-020-01200-0

Mantovani, N., Pizzolati, M., & Edge, D. (2017). Exploring the relationship between stigma and help-seeking for mental illness in African-descended faith communities in the UK. *Health Expectations*, 20(3), 373–384. doi: 10.1111/hex.12464.

Parker, L. L., & Harriger, J.A. (2020). Eating disorders and disordered eating behaviors in the LGBT population: a review of the literature. *Journal of Eating Disorders*, 8, art. 51. https://doi.org/10.1186/s40337-020-00327-y.

Razai, M., Osama, T., McKechnie, D. and Majeed, A. (2021). Covid-19 vaccine hesitancy among ethnic minority groups. *British Medical Journal*, 181(7), 1008–1011.

Sinha, S., & Warfa, N. (2013). Treatment of eating disorders among ethnic minorities in western settings: A systematic review. *Psychiatria Danubina*, 25(Suppl 2), S295–S299.

Strother, E., Lemberg, R., Stanford, S. C., & Turberville, D. (2012). Eating disorders in men: underdiagnosed, undertreated, and misunderstood. *Eating Disorders* [online], 20(5), 346–355. doi: https://doi.org/10.1080/10640266.2012.715512.

Swann, C., Pachter, L., Liverlight, E. & Gannon, M. (2021). Race and disordered eating: a narrative review of current literature. *Phase 1*, Paper 2. Thomas Jefferson University. https://jdc.jefferson.edu/si_hs_2023_phase1/2.

Thomas, T. (2020). NHS hospital admissions for eating disorders rise among ethnic minorities. *Guardian* [online], 18 October. www.theguardian.com/society/2020/oct/18/nhs-hospital-admissions-eating-disorders-rise-among-ethnic-minorities.

ANOREXIA NERVOSA
Dr Elizabeth McNaught

BACKGROUND

Anorexia nervosa (AN) is one of the most well-known eating disorders, but due to its secretive nature research into its prevalence can be a challenge. It is thought to be most common between the ages of 15 and 19 years (NICE, 2019) and can affect both males and females, with a lifetime prevalence of up to 4 per cent in females and 0.3 per cent in males (van Eeden et al., 2021). In children this female preponderance is not as marked (Zipfel et al., 2015). However, it has long been questioned whether the figures quoted for males are an under-representation and if we do not yet fully recognise how many men are affected. AN can affect people from all socio-economic and cultural backgrounds and has the highest mortality rate of any mental illness, due to a combination of the physical complications of starvation and the increased risk of suicide. The crude mortality rate has been reported to be 5.1 per 1,000 person years (van Eeden et al., 2021).

> By the time I started secondary school, I was obsessed with my body. I'd spend hours grabbing at my stomach and legs until my skin was raw, and sat crying in the changing rooms of the school uniform shop while I was furious at my changing proportions.
>
> Cara Lisette

We can start to understand how AN develops through the biopsychosocial model, considering the role of biological, psychological, and sociocultural elements.

DOI: 10.4324/9781003342762-4

BIOLOGICAL

Genetics are thought to play a significant role in the development of AN. Twin-based studies have demonstrated heritability estimates ranging between 0.28 to 0.74 (Bulik et al., 2019) and a concordance rate of 0.71 for monozygotic and 0.1 for dizygotic twins (Himmerich et al., 2019). In addition, family studies have identified that first degree relatives of those with AN have a tenfold increased lifetime risk of developing an eating disorder than those without (Himmerich et al., 2019).

There are many other biological risk factors, including:

- Perinatal factors
  - Chickenpox and rubella infections in pregnancy (Bakalar et al., 2015).
  - Maternal anaemia, diabetes, pre-eclampsia and placental infarction, neonatal cardiac problems, and hyporeactivity (Favaro et al., 2006).
- Puberty, particularly with a younger age of onset.
- Presence of autoimmune and autoinflammatory disorders in both the patient and their parents (Zerwas et al., 2017).

PSYCHOLOGICAL

Psychological risk factors describe elements of who we are as people and our personality. Many different psychological factors have been identified as influencing the development of AN. These include perfectionism (particularly self-orientated perfectionism – setting oneself high standards with a feeling of failure if one does not achieve them), global childhood rigidity, increased persistence (keeping going with something despite feeling tired or frustrated), sensitivity to punishment, increased harm avoidance and premorbid internalizing of problems in childhood (Bakalar et al., 2015), behavioural inflexibility, and body image dissatisfaction (Peterson, Fuller 2019).

In addition, the presence of comorbid mental illnesses, such as anxiety disorders, mood disorders, and obsessive compulsive disorder (OCD) (Peterson & Fuller, 2019), and personality disorders, have been linked to AN development.

SOCIOCULTURAL

Sociocultural risk factors describe the influences of the world around us. A perceived pressure to be thin, exposure to the media-driven "thin ideal", social comparison, and adverse life events have been identified as risk factors for AN (Bulik et al., 2019).

Other risk factors include exposure to dieting behaviour (e.g. through someone significant in their life), the presence of teasing or bullying, and having a limited social network (Peterson & Fuller, 2019).

Hobbies and professions can also have an impact on someone's risk, particularly if the activity has a focus on body shape and weight or if this confers an athletic advantage (e.g. modelling, dance, sport) (Kan & Treasure, 2019).

PRESENTATION

AN may present in a range of settings, such as health care, education, sports activities, and primary and secondary care. Due to the egosyntonic nature of the illness, people may not recognise that they are having issues and, if they do, they may feel so frightened of having their behaviours challenged that they will often go to great lengths to hide this.

> I remember crying for hours. Almost overnight my daughter became so distant, she had found an inner strength I could not compete with, a determination, stubbornness and cold attitude to me, her father, her siblings – it took us several months (if not years) to accept and work out how best to support our daughter.
>
> Nicky Smith

The central feature of AN is a restriction in food intake resulting in significant weight loss. People with AN will often be of low weight, with some profoundly underweight. However, they will often not recognise this and may perceive themselves as larger than they are. Their drive to control and limit their food intake becomes overwhelming, sometimes at the expense of education, employment, relationships, and social life.

> I was focused entirely on the numbers on the scales (I weighed myself twice a day) and the minimal amount of fruit juice that I allowed myself to drink. Each period of time I lasted without food, I wanted to test myself and last longer.
>
> Christina Taylor

Due to its secretive nature, spotting the signs may be a challenge. The ABCDE model can be used to help understand and look out for key features (Pollard, 2019):

- A – Absence
  A struggle to eat in public, maybe avoiding social events which involve food, and becoming socially withdrawn. Eating with other people is uncomfortable, so they choose to eating alone.
- B – Body
  Excessive focus on the size and shape of their body, presence of body-checking behaviours (repeated measuring or analysing their body in mirrors), distorted body image with intense fear of weight gain, a rapid change in their body size, which they may try to hide by wearing baggy clothing.
- C – Control
  A need to be in control of what they are eating (e.g. weighing out every portion of food). Trying to control the timing and preparation of food, with a reluctance to eat food prepared by other people.
- D – Diet
  Rigid restrictive food intake, presence of food rituals, reporting not to like food that they previously enjoyed (e.g. pasta, pizza), a change in dietary preferences (e.g. becoming a vegetarian or vegan, without the corresponding belief system).
- E – Exercise
  Engaging in excessive and obsessive exercise despite poor food intake, and a feeling of anxiety and distress if they cannot partake in their exercise routine. They may exercise beyond the point that most people would be able to manage, in relation to their food intake.

When I graduated, my anorexia got worse. University gave me structure and purpose. Those aspects of my life came to an abrupt end when I finished university. I felt lost, empty, and purposeless. It was the perfect mental climate for the anorexia to grow. And It did exactly that. By the time I was diagnosed, the illness had taken over my mind, body, and life.

Florence Greenwood

> While I had struggled with food and my body image for as long as I could remember, anorexia took hold swiftly and my life transformed within a few short months. I became isolated, obsessive, and terrified of any and all situations involving food.
>
> Laura Hanton

DIAGNOSIS

Doctors make a diagnosis of AN based on the DSM-5 (*Diagnostic and Statistical Manual of Mental Disorders*) and/or ICD-11 (*International Classification of Diseases*).

Diagnostic features drawn from these are (American Psychiatric Association, 2013; World Health Organization, 2022):

- Restriction of food intake resulting in a significantly low body weight.
  - Rapid weight loss may replace low body weight.
  - Low body weight is not due to lack of food availability or another medical condition.
  - In children and adolescents, they may present with a failure to gain weight instead of weight loss.
- Engagement in behaviours aimed to prevent weight gain.
  - Eating extremely slowly, purging behaviours (e.g. abuse of laxatives, diuretics, medication, fasting), behaviours aimed to increase energy expenditure (e.g. excessive exercise).
- A fear of weight gain.
- A disturbance in their view of their body shape or weight, with an overemphasis based on how they look.
  - They may see themselves as a normal or overweight and appear unable to recognise the serious implications of being underweight.
  - They may engage in repeated body-checking behaviours (regularly weighing themselves, measuring their body, or body checking in a mirror) or go to extreme lengths to avoid addressing their body shape (e.g. avoiding mirrors).

The ICD-11 categorises AN into different subtypes (anorexia with significantly low body weight, anorexia with dangerously low body weight, and anorexia in recovery with normal body weight), and the DSM-5 categorises it into two (restricting type and binge-eating/purging type).
(American Psychiatric Association, 2013; World Health Organization, 2022)

AN may develop comorbid with other mental illnesses. Comorbidity rates are estimated to be as high as 73.3 per cent, with the most common being mood disorders followed by anxiety disorders (Moskowitz & Weiselberg, 2017). Other common comorbid conditions include OCD (obsessive compulsive disorder), personality disorders, self-harm, alcohol, and substance abuse (more likely in binge/purge subtype than restricting) (Peterson & Fuller, 2019; Zipfel et al., 2015). Autism spectrum disorder (ASD) has also been strongly linked with AN, with some estimating a 16.3 per cent prevalence of ASD in AN (Inoue et al., 2021). The severity of the comorbidities is thought to increase with the severity of the eating disorder (Westmoreland et al., 2016).

CONSULTATION WITH A DOCTOR

Often the initial consultation will be with a GP. During this and future consultations, it is important for the doctor to build a good rapport. Sometimes this may be a challenge, due to the patient often feeling anxious and apprehensive about disclosing the truth of their eating disorder and worries around any potential treatments. They may also appear ambivalent to the disorder and the potential life-threatening complications. It can be challenging for the doctor, parents, and carers to manage this. It can be advantageous for the doctor to include other people (e.g. family and carers) in assessments, to gain a collateral history (Zipfel et al., 2015).

When the eating disorder was brought into the light, it fought like a rabid dog. Our beautiful, kind, compassionate, funny, sweet, daughter turned into a completely different child. No one can understand how awful it is, unless you've lived it and that's where it is so important to have a community of people around you who understand.
Rochelle Rouse

The doctor's assessment will consist of two parts: gaining a history and conducting a physical assessment.

HISTORY

"Taking a history" is the process whereby the doctor talks to the patient and gathers information. The doctor will often ask about current symptoms (the patient may be reluctant to disclose restrictive eating or purging behaviour but may report feeling irritable, dizzy, faint, constipated, etc.). They may want to find out how long it has been going on, when it started, and how the patient is feeling about it. They may ask, directly or covertly, what the patient is currently eating, how they feel about food and their body, and if they are engaging in any compensatory behaviours such as vomiting or abuse of medication.

The doctor may also wish to check for any physical symptoms which may have developed due to the disorder, such as dizziness or palpitations. They will often screen for any comorbid mental illness, such as depression and self-harm behaviours.

ASSESSMENT

A doctor will need to conduct a thorough physical assessment to look for any complications that may have developed. This will often be through an examination (checking their blood pressure, heart rate, and temperature; listening to their heart and lungs, feeling their abdomen). They may also wish to conduct an ECG (electrocardiogram) and blood tests.

Doctors will want to weigh the patient. Someone living with AN will likely find this experience stressful, and therefore it should be approached sensitively (including a discussion as to whether or not the patient would like to know their weight). When weighing someone in this situation, consideration should be given to behaviours that someone with AN may use to falsify their weight, such as drinking large volumes of fluid (water loading), wearing heavy clothes and shoes, or having weights in their pockets. If they need weight monitoring (e.g. weekly weighing), then this should be done in a controlled manner, weighing the person at the same time each week and in the same clothes (ideally lightweight clothing).

This assessment is important, as it identifies any physical complications that may have developed, because AN can affect nearly every organ in the body. The majority of these effects are as a result of malnutrition and often resolve with weight restoration. Physical complications include the following (Chidiac, 2019; Neale & Hudson, 2020; Westmoreland et al., 2016; Zipfel et al., 2015):

- Brain
  - Brain atrophy.
- Cardiovascular system
  - Bradycardia (low heart rate), hypotension (low blood pressure), postural hypotension (drop in blood pressure on standing). Tachycardia (increased heart rate) is uncommon and may indicate an increased risk of arrhythmia and sudden cardiac death.
  - ECG changes.
  - Severe AN can influence the heart's structure, with a reduction in the amount of heart muscle.
- Gastrointestinal
  - Irritation of the oesophagus, resulting in Barrett's oesophagus and dysphagia (difficulty in swallowing).
  - Slowed gastric emptying (resulting in feeling full and bloated quickly) and colonic function (resulting in constipation).
  - Risk of gastric dilation and stomach ulcers.
  - Abnormal liver function tests.
- Haematological
  - Anaemia (low haemoglobin), leukopaenia (low white cell count) and thrombocytopaenia (low platelets).
- Growth and bone health
  - Being underweight can result in growth impairment.
  - When someone is underweight, they are at risk of developing osteoporosis (thinning of the bones), which is thought to affect up to 21 per cent of people with AN, placing them at an increased risk of fractures.
  - The risk of fractures can be raised for many years and may not be fully reversed by weight restoration.
- Skin
  - Skin changes include dry skin (xerosis) and abnormal hair growth (lanugo) on the spine and side of the face.
- Puberty
  - People may experience a delay in puberty or a reversion to a pre-pubertal state, with females experiencing a loss of their periods (amenorrhea).
  - AN can have a long-term impact on female fertility.

- Electrolyte disturbance
  - The electrolyte levels in the blood can be affected by starvation and purging behaviours, the most common changes being hyponatraemia (low sodium), hypokalaemia (low potassium), and renal failure.

> About the impact of starvation on the brain ... Nobody in treatment explained this to me. I had to seek it out for myself. I just couldn't reconcile the person in front of me with the person I knew. I knew that her behaviours were bizarre and had a hunch that she wasn't choosing to be this way, but I had to find that out for myself, hours of Googling.
> Suzanne Baker

POTENTIAL FOR BLIND SPOTS, MISDIAGNOSES, AND BIASES

When someone is assessed for AN, the doctor will often consider alternative "differential" diagnoses – other conditions which may explain the symptoms they are presenting with. These may include problems with the gastrointestinal system, infections, systemic disorders (e.g. systemic lupus erythematosus), effects of medication, malignancies, and other mental illnesses (e.g. anxiety disorders, mood disorders, ARFID).

Body mass index (BMI) is often still used in clinical practice to assess the degree of risk, with a lower BMI correlating with increased risk of physical complications and harm. A BMI of less than 18.5 kg/m^2 in adults, and below the fifth percentile in children, is considered to be underweight. However, BMI can be unhelpful in a range of situations, and many eating disorder campaigners are calling to remove it from the assessment in eating disorders. It has been suggested that the risk of being physically unwell is more related to degree of weight loss rather than absolute weight (Neale & Hudson, 2020), so someone may be at risk of significant physical harm while being at a "normal" BMI.

Males with AN are often misdiagnosed. They may be viewed as being "athletic", into their health and fitness, or their changing and slimming body shape is put down to growth and adolescence. This factor, in addition to the stigma that AN only affects young girls, means that males will often go undiagnosed for significant periods of time and may find it harder to access support and treatment.

Anorexia was something that happened to other people, in soaps, glossy magazines, and tabloid newspapers. The "A bomb" was far too extreme to explain what I was doing.

Dave Chawner

TREATMENT

Following an initial assessment if AN is suspected, a referral should be made to the eating disorder specialists. The guidance is clear: single measures, such as BMI and illness duration, should not be used to decide if treatment will be offered.

Treatment is often provided by a multi-disciplinary team (MDT), including a physician and specialists in psychology, psychiatry, and nutrition (Chidiac, 2019). Alongside psychological therapy, patients should have a dietary assessment and support, and may require an age-appropriate oral multivitamin and multimineral supplement.

AN can produce a significant impact and burden on families and carers, which can be challenging and have a damaging effect on family relationships (Kan & Treasure, 2019). Families and carers may need an assessment of their own needs and mental health, and support should be offered as needed.

I was glad that she had a diagnosis and was being referred for help. I was scared for her and of losing her. I felt guilty for not doing something sooner and for not being stricter with her eating and exercise. I felt embarrassed, that I hadn't realised how ill she was. I felt angry at the world. I felt humiliated by comments from others, such as "Well, just make her eat." I felt like I was the worst mother in the world and if she had died, it would have been my fault.

Chris Avenell

The mainstay of treatment for AN is talking therapies combined with nutritional restoration. Reversal of a "starvation state" is important due to the damaging effects of starvation on both the body and the mind, worsening the eating pathology (Kan, Treasure 2019). This is often done under the guidance of a dietitian and may involve a gradual increase in volume of food eaten. For example, a person with AN may start by eating small volumes of food at each meal, and snacks, increasing this over time (to help prevent refeeding syndrome).

Another reason I never did anything about it was because I didn't know how to talk about mental health. I know that sounds daft, but I'd never been given the communication tools to talk about mental health. Telling someone to "just talk" about their mental health is a bit like an ironmonger chucking you some goggles, a slab of iron, and a blowtorch, and telling you to "just weld". If you haven't taught someone how to do something, why would you expect them to know where to start?

Dave Chawner

People living with AN will find increasing their food intake immensely stressful and difficult, and this may worsen their disordered thoughts. This needs to be carefully monitored, and care and support provided.

There has been a lot of discussion around the use of medication, with some suggesting that low-dose antipsychotics may be of benefit in managing the delusional beliefs seen in AN (Westmoreland et al., 2016). However, the NICE (National Institute for Health and Care Excellence) guidance states that medication should not be used as a sole treatment.

NICE sets out treatment guidelines and the following is adapted from this (NICE, 2017):

TALKING THERAPY

Adults may be offered one of three talking therapies: individualised eating-disorder-focused cognitive behavioural therapy (CBT-ED), Maudsley Anorexia Nervosa Treatment for Adults (MANTRA), and specialist supportive clinical management (SSCM).

During CBT-ED sessions, the patient will make their own treatment plan to address the underlying causes of their disorder. They will work with the therapist to discuss nutrition and the consequences of being underweight while also discussing other psychological symptoms, including mood, body image, and self-esteem. In addition, they discuss tools to aid in relapse prevention. During CBT-ED, the person living through AN is empowered to have control over their eating disorder and will be asked to complete self-monitoring of their food intake, thoughts, and behaviours, and to engage in homework to implement what they are learning within their daily life.

MANTRA treatment is based on a workbook and involves encouraging and motivating the person living with AN to engage in treatment, looking at nutrition, managing their symptoms, and changing their behaviours. They will be encouraged to develop an identity separate to the AN, and family and carers may be involved to help support recovery.

> Anorexia would say to leave the crumbs, so I'd eat them. It would scream to take the stairs, so I'd take the lift instead. I proved anorexia wrong every single time. Eating disorders are liars, and the more you prove that to be true, the stronger you become.
>
> Naomi Parnell

SSCM therapy focuses on helping the patient to understand the relationship between their eating patterns and the symptoms they are experiencing. They will be given psychoeducation around the disorder, and nutritional advice. They are encouraged to restore their weight to a healthy level.

If any of these three treatments are ineffective or unacceptable, they should be offered eating-disorder-focused focal psychodynamic therapy (FPT). This therapy is a three-phase treatment that looks at addressing the anorexic behaviours and beliefs, focusing on relationships with others and how these interact with their eating behaviours, and finally on how to transfer learning points from therapy into their daily life.

In children and young people, the treatment offered is often slightly different, the first line of therapy being anorexia-nervosa-focused family therapy. During this therapy, the family have sessions together (the children and young people may also opt to have some individual sessions). The emphasis is on the family to help the person to recover. Early on, the parents and carers take a key role in supporting the young person with food and eating, and over time this responsibility shifts to the young person. If this treatment is ineffective or contraindicated, the other options are CBT-ED and adolescent-focused psychotherapy for anorexia nervosa (AFP-AN), both of which are run as individual sessions.

Further information about treatment can be found in Chapter 11.

REFEEDING SYNDROME

During the process of nutritional restoration, a person living with AN is at risk of developing refeeding syndrome, and this risk is highest in the first two weeks. When the body is in a state of starvation, it turns from an anabolic (building-up) to a catabolic (breaking-down) state. With the resumption of food intake, this reverses, and as a result the body uses more electrolytes. One of these is phosphate and with increased body needs the levels of phosphate (and other micronutrients) in the bloodstream fall. The resulting electrolyte imbalance can place someone at increased risk of developing potentially fatal heart rhythm abnormalities.

HOSPITAL ADMISSIONS

Sometimes people need admission to hospital as part of their care, this may be an admission to a general medical hospital for medical stabilisation or to a psychiatric hospital for day or in-patient treatment. Higher risk patients often need the latter (Kan & Treasure, 2019). Previously long hospital stays were used, however recently there has been a move to a "stepped care method" where the inpatient stay is shorter and then followed by day care treatment (Kan & Treasure, 2019). This has been found to be just as effective as longer inpatient treatment and is more economical (Zipfel et al., 2015).

Treating comorbidities can have an impact on AN recovery, but mood and anxiety-related symptoms may also improve with weight restoration (Neale & Hudson, 2020).

OUTCOMES

Recovery is always possible, although it is estimated that less than half of people with AN recover and around one third have a varied course (Moskowitz et al., 2017). A critical three-year window is often discussed, whereby, after three years of the disorder, recovery is harder and rates of this decline. Adult studies have shown a five- to six-year journey to remission (Zipfel et al., 2015). Mortality rate is thought to be lower, and the outcome better, for children and adolescents (Chidiac, 2019). Death is more likely in those whose weight rapidly changes (rather than those with a persistently low weight) and those who engage in frequent purging behaviours, particularly when at a low weight (Morris & Twaddle, 2007).

SUMMARY

- Anorexia nervosa (AN) is most common between the ages of 15 and 19 and often affects females more than males.
- It is thought that AN is underdiagnosed in males and the prevalence is suspected to be higher than that quoted.
- Biological risk factors include genetics, perinatal factors, puberty, and the presence of autoimmune disorders.
- Psychological risk factors include perfectionism, global childhood rigidity, and harm avoidance.
- Sociocultural risk factors include exposure to the "thin ideal", adverse life events, and certain hobbies and professions based around body shape and weight.
- People living with AN will often go to great lengths to hide their disorder, as they feel fearful and frightened of having their behaviours challenged.
- They key features of AN are a restriction of food intake and significantly low weight, alongside a distorted view of their body shape and weight, often seeing themselves as larger than they are.
- AN is commonly comorbid with other mental health conditions, typically mood and anxiety disorders.
- The initial assessment of AN is often done by a GP and consists of a history (a discussion with the person to understand their current symptoms, duration of illness, and food intake), followed by an examination to look for any complications which may have developed.
- BMI is often used to assess the risk in AN, although this can be unhelpful in a range of situations. It has been suggested that degree of weight loss is better at assessing risk than absolute weight.
- Treatment is often provided by eating disorder specialists and consists of a combination of talking therapy and nutritional restoration, while being cautious of the risk of developing refeeding syndrome.
- Recovery from AN is always possible. A critical three-year window is often discussed, and after three years of the illness recovery is harder and rates of this decline.

REFERENCES

American Psychiatric Association. (2013). *Diagnostic and statistical manual of mental disorders: DSM-5*, 5th edition. Washington, DC: American Psychiatric Publishing.

Bakalar, J. L., Shank, L. M., Vannucci, A., et al. (2015). Recent advances in developmental and risk factor research on eating disorders. *Current Psychiatry Reports* 17(6), 42. https://doi.org/10.1007/s11920-015-0585-x.

Bulik, C. M., Flatt, R., Abbaspour, A., & Carroll, I. (2019). Reconceptualizing anorexia nervosa. *Psychiatry and Clinical Neurosciences*. 73(9), 518–525. https://doi.org/10.1111/pcn.12857.

Chidiac C. W. (2019). An update on the medical consequences of anorexia nervosa. *Current Opinion in Pediatrics, 31*(4), 448–453. https://doi.org/10.1097/MOP.0000000000000755.

Favaro, A., Tenconi, E., & Santonastaso, P. (2006). Perinatal factors and the risk of developing anorexia nervosa and bulimia nervosa. *Archives of General Psychiatry*, 63(1), 82–88. https://doi.org/10.1001/archpsyc.63.1.82.

Himmerich, H., Bentley, J., Kan, C., & Treasure, J. (2019). Genetic risk factors for eating disorders: an update and insights into pathophysiology. *Therapeutic Advances in Psychopharmacology*, 9. https://doi.org/10.1177/2045125318814734

Inoue, T., Otani, R., Iguchi, T., Ishii, R., Uchida, S., Okada, A., … & Sakuta, R. (2021). Prevalence of autism spectrum disorder and autistic traits in children with anorexia nervosa and avoidant/restrictive food intake disorder. *BioPsychoSocial Medicine*, 15(1), 9. https://doi.org/10.1186/s13030-021-00212-3.

Kan, C., & Treasure, J. (2019). Recent research and personalized treatment of anorexia nervosa. *Psychiatric Clinics of North America*, 42(1), 11–19. https://doi.org/10.1016/j.psc.2018.10.010.

Morris, J., & Twaddle, S. (2007). Anorexia nervosa. *British Medical Journal*, 334(7599), 894–898. https://doi.org/10.1136/bmj.39171.616840.BE.

Moskowitz, L., & Weiselberg, E. (2017). Anorexia nervosa/atypical anorexia nervosa. *Current Problems in Pediatric and Adolescent Health Care*, 47(4), 70–84. https://doi.org/10.1016/j.cppeds.2017.02.003.

National Institute for Health and Care Excellence. (2017). Eating disorders: recognition and *treatment*. NICE guideline [NG69]. London: NICE. www.nice.org.uk/guidance/ng69/chapter/Recommendations.

National Institute for Health and Care Excellence. (2019). Eating disorders. NICE. https://cks.nice.org.uk/topics/eating-disorders/

Neale, J., & Hudson, L. D. (2020). Anorexia nervosa in adolescents. *British Journal of Hospital Medicine*, 81(6), 1–8. https://doi.org/10.12968/hmed.2020.0099.

Peterson, K., & Fuller, R. (2019). Anorexia nervosa in adolescents: an overview. *Nursing*, 49(10), 24–30. https://doi.org/10.1097/01.NURSE.0000580640.43071.15.

Pollard, N. J. (2019). The ABCDE tool for spotting the early signs of an eating disorder. *The Family Files*, 4. FamilyMentalWealth.com/FamilyFiles.

van Eeden, A. E., van Hoeken, D., & Hoek, H. W. (2021). Incidence, prevalence and mortality of anorexia nervosa and bulimia nervosa. *Current Opinion in Psychiatry*, 34(6), 515–524. https://doi.org/10.1097/YCO.0000000000000739.

Westmoreland, P., Krantz, M. J., & Mehler, P. S. (2016). Medical complications of anorexia nervosa and bulimia. *American Journal of Medicine*, 129(1), 30–37. https://doi.org/10.1016/j.amjmed.2015.06.031.

World Health Organization. (2022). *ICD-11: international classification of diseases*, 11th revision. https://icd.who.int/.

Zerwas S., Larsen J. T., Petersen L., Thornton L. M., Quaranta, M., Koch, S.V., … & Bulik, C.M. (2017). Eating disorders, autoimmune, and autoinflammatory disease. *Pediatrics*, 140(6), e20162089. doi:10.1542/peds.2016-2089.

Zipfel, S., Giel, K. E., Bulik, C. M., Hay, P., & Schmidt, U. (2015). Anorexia nervosa: aetiology, assessment, and treatment. *The Lancet: Psychiatry*, 2(12), 1099–1111. https://doi.org/10.1016/S2215-0366(15)00356-9.

5

BULIMIA NERVOSA
Dr Elizabeth McNaught

BACKGROUND

Bulimia nervosa (BN) is more common than anorexia nervosa (AN) and has a lifetime prevalence of up to 3 per cent in females and more than 1 per cent in males (the lower prevalence in males may be influenced by limited studies), with a peak age of onset being later than AN, at 15–29 years (van Eeden et al., 2021). It has been thought to have a female:male ratio of 3:1 (Castillo & Weiselberg, 2017), but can affect anyone, regardless of their age, gender, sexuality, and ethnicity. BN carries with it an increased mortality rate, in most part due to physical complications of purging behaviour and comorbid mental illness, in particular self-harm behaviour and suicidality. The weighted crude mortality rate is estimated to be around 1.74 per 1,000 person years (NICE, 2019).

It has been suggested that between 24 and 31 per cent of people with BN have been diagnosed with AN earlier in their life (Wade, 2019), and up to 40 per cent are thought to have significant comorbid mental illness or suicidality (Gorrell & Grange, 2019).

Understanding the risk factors and how BN develops can be examined through the biopsychosocial model, considering the role of biological, psychological, and sociocultural elements. Several risk factors are shared between AN and BN, and between BN and binge eating disorder (BED).

BIOLOGICAL

The role of genetics and family history in the development of BN has been well studied, with an estimated heritability of 0.6 (Bulik et al., 2019). In addition, having a family history of mental illness

DOI: 10.4324/9781003342762-5

(particularly bipolar disorder, anxiety, or a previous eating disorder) increases the risk of BN (Castillo & Weiselberg, 2017). For example, the relative risk for females of developing BN is 4.2 if they have a first-degree relative with AN and 4.4 if they have a first-degree relative with BN (Himmerich et al., 2019).

As with AN, other biological risk factors have been linked to BN, including:

- Perinatal factors.
  - Problems with the placenta, hyporeactivity in the baby, low birth weight (Favaro et al., 2006).
- As in AN, BN has been linked to puberty, which is thought to activate a genetic vulnerability.
- Having a higher body mass index (BMI) (Wade, 2019).
- Presence of autoimmune disorders either in the person with BN or in their parent (Zerwas et al., 2017).

PSYCHOLOGICAL

Psychological risk factors include who we are as people, how our minds work, and how we think. Those that have been linked to BN include impulsivity (the tendency to act on instinct without thinking through the consequences), internalisation of the thin ideal, and weight and shape concerns (Nitsch et al., 2021). BN has also been linked to difficulties in emotional regulation – for example, those with BN may have difficulty in being aware of, and accepting, different emotional states (Wade, 2019).

Other psychological factors that have been identified include low self-esteem, low mood, social anxiety (Castillo et al., 2017), greater novelty seeking behaviour, increased harm avoidance (Bakalar et al., 2015), and increased sensitivity to reward (the tendency to pursue a behaviour, such as eating food, to gain positive reinforcement) (Eneva et al., 2017).

> Looking back, I feel I developed my eating disorder as a response to the uncertainty in my life and as a coping mechanism for my growing anxiety. I sought comfort in my eating disorder behaviours as a way of feeling in control, in a world where I felt out of control.
>
> Kirsty Stapledon

SOCIOCULTURAL

Sociocultural risk factors (those that are present in the surrounding world) contribute to the development of BN. Among those identified are childhood obesity, weight-related teasing, and having a history of disordered eating in a parent (this may take the form of dieting or overeating) (Hilbert et al., 2014). In addition, people will often report that a disturbance in their own eating pattern precedes the onset of BN – for example, dieting or binge eating behaviour (Hilbert et al., 2014).

Stressful life events and childhood trauma have long been discussed as risk factors (Nitsch et al., 2021), particularly sexual abuse (Hilbert et al., 2014), but also low social support (Stice et al., 2017), physical neglect, and having a home life that is felt to be critical in nature (maybe in the form of negative comments about the person's body shape or weight, or excessive emphasis placed on this).

PRESENTATION

BN may present in a range of settings, including health care, education, sports activities, and primary and secondary care. Patients may feel high levels of shame and stigma around their symptoms and thus feel hesitant to disclose what is happening.

> When I reflect on why I felt so unable to use the word "bulimia", I feel it was due to the shame and stigma I felt around the bingeing and purging behaviours. By acknowledging it for what it was, people would be let into my deepest vulnerabilities, and this terrified me ... I invalidated myself when I felt I didn't look like a person with an eating disorder or wasn't "ill enough".
>
> Kirsty Stapledon

The central feature of BN is the presence of the "binge–purge" cycle. People with BN may report going through a period of dietary restriction (often with the primary aim of weight loss). They may then experience certain "triggers", such as low mood, interpersonal stress, and body dissatisfaction. These often lead to a binge eating episode, resulting in eating large volumes of food in a short space of time. A person with BN may feel out of control and in a trancelike state, often feeling numb and unable to stop themselves eating. This often occurs in private and is followed by intense feelings of guilt and shame.

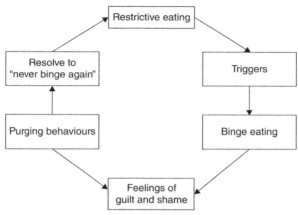

Figure 5.1   An example of the binge–purge–restrict cycle of bulimia nervosa.

> Whilst many components of eating disorders are insidious, creeping on you slowly, convincing you you are in control rather than the eating disorder, the nature of bulimia – bingeing and purging – meant that pretty quickly I knew a line had been crossed.
>
> Marina

Binge eating is then followed by purging behaviours, methods used to prevent weight gain. These may take the form of self-induced vomiting (most common), abuse of medications (laxatives, diuretics, amphetamines, prescribed medications such as levothyroxine), fasting (going for prolonged periods of time, often eight hours or more, not eating), or excessive exercise. Following this, people will often resolve to "never binge again" and return to their restrictive pattern of eating.

> The eating disorder controlled me, isolated me, and could never be satisfied. It prayed on my low self-esteem, and it made me feel as though I was never enough.... Physically, my body felt under duress, exhausted and damaged and yet the eating disorder kept me in a protective shell of denial.
>
> Kirsty Stapledon

> My eating disorder thrived in secrecy and made me quite a selfish and manipulative person; I felt completely detached from my former identity ... I pushed my family away and this had a huge impact on my relationship with my parents at this time. The eating disorder had gone from just being a tenant in my head, to lodging in our house, and to having a place laid at the table.
>
> Kirsty Stapledon

The ABCDE model can be used to help understand and look out for key features (Pollard, 2019).

- A – Absence
  Binge eating occurs in secrecy, away from other people. People may disappear for prolonged periods of time after eating, such as to their bedroom or bathroom. They may have long showers after eating, to disguise purging behaviour. They may feel hesitant about eating in front of others and become socially withdrawn.
- B – Body
  Excessive focus on the size and shape of their body, distorted body image, a rapid change in their body size (most people with BN are of normal weight, but binge eating may cause weight gain and purging may result in significant weight loss).
- C – Control
  During a period of binge eating, they may feel out of control with food, feeling that they are eating in a rapid and mechanical way and can't stop themselves. They may then move to a period of restriction, when they feel a need to be in control of their food intake and often limit what they will eat.
- D – Diet
  During a period of being eating, they may eat food that is easy to consume (with little preparation) and easy to purge. They may eat food they would otherwise avoid, typically high-fat and high-sugar foods. This may be followed by the restrictive period, when they may limit their food intake and avoid typically "fattening" foods. Family may notice food going missing or empty food packets in their bedroom.
- E – Exercise
  Exercise may be used as a method of purging. They may engage in excessive and obsessive exercise, which may have a significant

impact on their everyday life and ability to function. They also may feel high levels of anxiety if this was interrupted or prevented.

> The hardest part of struggling with bulimia is definitely the shame and embarrassment. This can be isolating and push one away from friends/ social networks, leading you to become even more dependent on the eating disorder. It also stopped me from reaching out for a long time.
>
> Marina

DIAGNOSIS

Doctors make a diagnosis of BN based on the DSM-5 (*Diagnostic and Statistical Manual of Mental Disorders*) and/or ICD-11 (*International Classification of Diseases*) (American Psychiatric Association, 2013; World Health Organization, 2022).

Diagnostic features drawn from these are:

- Recurrent episodes of binge eating behaviours.
    - These are episodes where someone will eat a large volume of food that is more than most people would eat.
    - During these episodes, people feel out of control and unable to stop or limit what they are eating.
    - These overeating episodes often occur during a short period of time – typically two hours.
- Recurrent episodes of compensatory behaviours to prevent weight gain.
- Preoccupation with body shape and weight which has a significant impact on how they feel about themselves and their self-worth.
    - They may engage in body-checking behaviours, or actions to prevent seeing their body, like those seen in AN.
- These behaviours result in marked distress, which has a significant impact on functioning.
- Behaviours must not occur during a diagnosis of AN (they are mutually exclusive). If they do, then the AN diagnosis will override that of the BN.

> Bulimia really erodes your self-image. It is hard to feel confident when you spend so much time kneeling in front of the toilet.
>
> Marina

BN is commonly comorbid with other mental illnesses, including mood disorders, anxiety disorders, substance abuse, attention–deficit hyperactivity disorder (ADHD), and personality disorders. The presence of a comorbid personality disorder (the most common being emotionally unstable personality disorder) is linked to a worse outcome (Westmoreland et al., 2016). People with BN are also at increased risk of self-harm and suicidal thoughts and behaviours, and it has been estimated that they are eight times more likely to die by suicide than the general population (Nitsch et al., 2021).

CONSULTATION WITH A DOCTOR

People with BN will often initially present to their GP, and their first consultation will be in this setting. People may self-present, or be brought in by concerned family members. However, some may present acutely unwell to hospital (or other health care setting) with a disturbance in their electrolyte levels, due to complications of the disorder. Because of the stigma and shame, people may feel reluctant to disclose what is happening, partially due to the misbelief that people with an eating disorder are "underweight". However, most people with BN will be of normal or above normal weight (Castillo & Weiselberg, 2017).

> I often hear token phrases, like the hardest part is reaching out for help, but the hardest thing has been reaching out and trying to communicate that things aren't okay, only to be met with waiting lists, or be told that I'm fine due to a body mass index [BMI].
>
> Marina

The doctor's assessment will consist of two parts: gaining a history and conducting a physical assessment.

HISTORY

During the process of "taking a history", a doctor will talk to the patient to understand more about what is going on and what their current symptoms are. People with BN may feel embarrassed to disclose their binge eating episodes due to a fear of being viewed as "greedy" or having a "lack of control".

> The nature of eating disorders meant I could always convince myself it wasn't bad enough yet, that I didn't really have a problem but just lacked control or willpower – that it was all a matter of pulling myself together.
>
> Marina

The doctor will want to get a good understanding of what the binge–purge cycle is like, and may ask questions about what is typically eaten during an episode of binge eating, how long this takes, how the person feels, and how frequently these episodes are happening. They may then want to understand more about the compensatory behaviours. People with BN may be reluctant to disclose these, due to fear of them being stopped.

The doctor may also wish to check for any physical symptoms which may have developed due to the disorder, such as dizziness or palpitations. They will often screen for any comorbid mental illness, especially thoughts of self-harm or suicide.

ASSESSMENT

A doctor will need to conduct a thorough physical assessment to look for any complications that may have developed. This will be through an examination (checking their blood pressure, heart rate and temperature, listening to their heart and lungs, and feeling their abdomen). They may also wish to conduct an ECG (electrocardiogram) and blood tests.

This assessment is important, identifying any physical complications that may have developed because of restrictive eating or purging behaviours. The most common purging behaviours are vomiting or abuse of laxatives, and the physical complications are different for each. Most complications can be reversed with cessation of eating disorder behaviours. Physical complications from self-induced vomiting include the following (Castillo & Weiselberg, 2017; Gibson et al., 2019; Nitsch et al., 2021; Westmoreland et al., 2016):

- Eyes
  - Subconjunctival haemorrhages.
- Teeth and mouth
  - Loss of dental enamel, increased teeth sensitivity, and increased incidence of dental caries (which is irreversible).

- People who engage in self-induced vomiting are advised to avoid brushing their teeth straight after vomiting. Instead, they are encouraged to wash their mouth with water and later use fluoride mouthwash and horizontal gentle brushing.
- Enlarged salivary glands
  - This often develops three to four days after stopping vomiting and can be distressing for people, due to the fact their face shape changes. It will reverse with time, but this can be aided by the use of anti-inflammatory medication, warmth, and sour sweets.
- Gastrointestinal
  - Gastric reflux and dysphagia (difficulty swallowing).
  - Haematemesis (vomiting of blood) due to a tear in the oesophagus.
  - (Very rarely) Oesophageal rupture.
- Respiratory
  - Reflux of gastric acid can irritate the larynx, resulting in inflammation of the vocal folds, a hoarse voice, and a chronic cough. There is a risk of aspirating vomit, resulting in an aspirational pneumonia.
- Skin
  - Russell's sign – calluses may develop on the back of the hands due to self-induced vomiting.
- Endocrine
  - Excessive vomiting can influence the menstrual cycle, resulting in irregular periods.
- Electrolyte disturbance
  - Vomiting results in a loss of stomach acid and electrolytes, which may result in a metabolic alkalosis and hypokalaemia (low potassium).

> Potassium is used in nearly every cell in the body and having low levels can have dangerous effects. The most worrying one is cardiac arrhythmia (abnormal heart rhythms), which can be fatal. These may be seen on an ECG.

Physical complications from laxative abuse include the following (Castillo & Weisleberg, (Gibson et al., 2017, 2019; Westmoreland et al., 2016),

- Gastrointestinal
  - Rectal prolapse, haemorrhoids and haematochezia (rectal bleeding).
  - Long-term use of stimulant laxatives (such as senna) can result in damage to the nerves that supply the colon. This may result in a condition called "cathartic colon syndrome", where the colon can no longer move faecal matter through resulting in severe constipation. People may end up needing surgery.
  - Melanosis coli – benign discoloration of the colon due to chronic laxative abuse.
- Electrolyte disturbance.
  - Excessive use of laxatives often has little effect on body weight, but can result in a loss of body fluid and electrolytes, which can result in metabolic acidosis initially and then, over time, a metabolic alkalosis and hypokalaemia (low potassium).

POTENTIAL FOR BLIND SPOTS, MISDIAGNOSES, AND BIASES

When someone is assessed for BN, the doctor will often consider alternative "differential" diagnoses – other conditions which may explain the symptoms they are presenting with. These may include problems with the gastrointestinal system, medication, disorders of the thyroid, infectious diseases, metabolic disorders such as diabetes, and other mental illnesses.

When people with an eating disorder engage in purging behaviours, they will often label themselves as "bulimic". However, it is important to recognise the context to make a diagnosis of BN and the need of the binge–purge cycle in the presentation. Purging behaviour is not specific to BN, as it can occur in AN and purging disorder (Castillo & Weiselberg, 2017).

BN is often viewed as less serious than AN. This is further confounded by the assumption that people are not "underweight", like in AN. However, as we have seen from the potential complications, the impact of purging behaviours is in no way benign. Regardless of their weight, the risk of death from electrolyte disturbance remains significant.

> Bulimia can often feel like a failed or lesser eating disorder, so challenging this in myself and trying to recognise I deserve help and that this isn't my fault ... is definitely a work in progress.
>
> Marina

It is important to note a difference between subjective and objective binge eating. In the former, people may feel that they are eating a lot, but in reality they are still eating within normal limits. This may be like having a whole pizza and crisps on a Friday night, feeling like you have overdone it. In this experience, the eating of the food was enjoyable and people felt full but satisfied after, whereas in an objective binge people are eating more than would be considered a normal amount of food. This is not an enjoyable experience – they feel trapped eating in a rapid and compulsive way, often not tasting the food they are eating. In these situations, they tend only to stop eating when they physically cannot eat any more, which is followed by intense feelings of guilt and shame.

TREATMENT

Following an initial assessment if BN is suspected, a referral should be made to the eating disorder specialists. Treatment should be provided via a multidisciplinary team (MDT) including a physician, therapist, and dietitian (Castillo & Weiselberg, 2017). The initial treatment is to ensure medical stabilisation, and if electrolyte disturbance has been identified this will need to be managed according to its severity.

> If someone has developed hypokalaemia, they may be at increased risk of further episodes and so may need frequent monitoring with repeated blood tests.
>
> (Castillo & Weiselberg, 2017)

The mainstay of treatment is through psychological therapy, the aim being to break the binge–purge cycle and restore a balanced eating pattern through eating regular meals during the day. People with BN will often be fearful of this method. They may have an underlying desire to restrict their food intake for weight loss, and so feel worried that eating "normally" may result in weight gain. It is important to explain that acting on the temptation to restrict risks perpetuating the eating disorder through exacerbating the binge–purge cycles.

I began to realise that the values and goals of the eating disorder did not align with my personal values. I started to understand that, to have improved quality of life and accomplish any of my future aspirations, I needed to make a change.

Kirsty Stapledon

There has been much discussion around the use of medication in BN. In the UK, the NICE (National Institute for Health and Care Excellence) guidelines state that medication should not be used as a sole treatment for BN. However, the USA's FDA (Food and Drug Administration) has licensed Fluoxetine (a type of selective serotonin reuptake inhibitor – SSRI) following findings that it is useful in the treatment of BN (Nitsch et al., 2021), through its effects on the feelings of satiety (Westmoreland et al., 2016). Other medication that has been studied in treatment includes topiramate and Lisdexamfetamine (Castillo & Weiselberg, 2017).

NICE sets out treatment guidelines, and the following is adapted from this (NICE, 2017):

TALKING THERAPY

Adults may be offered treatment with bulimia-nervosa-focused guided self-help. This uses cognitive behavioural therapy-based (CBT-based) self-help materials, often in the form of a book, and involves the monitoring of food intake and eating disorder behaviours, developing a regular eating pattern, and helping people to think through the causes of their disorder and develop healthier coping strategies. This treatment should be accompanied by individual supportive sessions.

If this is ineffective or unacceptable, they should be offered individual eating-disorder-focused CBT (CBT-ED). This is offered to the person with BN on a one-to-one basis, the initial phase being focused on education, developing engagement with treatment, and establishing a regular eating pattern. This is followed by monitoring their thoughts, feelings, and behaviours and addressing and challenging the eating disorder thought processes. They are then supported in maintaining positive changes and preventing a relapse.

The treatment offered to children and young people is often slightly different, with the first line therapy being bulimia-nervosa-focused family therapy (FT-BN). Treatment is offered in a family group setting: they receive education about the disorder, and support in helping the young person to develop regular eating patterns. Over the course of treatment, the aim is to support the young person in developing independence in managing their eating and preventing relapse. The young person should partake in self-monitoring of their thoughts and behaviours, and the family sessions should be supplemented by some individual sessions.

If this is ineffective or unacceptable, the young person should be offered CBT-ED, which is similar to that offered to an adult.

Further information about treatment can be found in Chapter 11.

OUTCOMES

Recovery is always possible. The disorder has a lower mortality rate than AN and will often display a relapsing and remitting course, with 30–60 per cent estimated to make a full recovery after treatment (NICE, 2019). The outcome is better in adolescents than adults, and good prognostic indicators include an earlier age of onset, shorter duration of symptoms, and positive parent–child relationships (Castillo & Weiselberg, 2017).

When considering outcomes, the presence of an earlier diagnosis of AN reduced the recovery likelihood (Wade, 2019), and those who have a comorbid mental illness also have a worse outcome, with increased risk of death (Westmoreland et al., 2016).

> I now see that berating myself for my struggles was completely unproductive and find solace in knowing that, whilst I may not be able to control all my circumstances, I can control how I react to them. Every time I can challenge the eating disorder voice, which still rears its ugly head in times of high stress, it becomes a little quieter and my hope for a life eating-disorder-free becomes a little greater.
>
> Kirsty Stapledon

SUMMARY

- Bulimia nervosa (BN) is more common than anorexia nervosa (AN) and has a peak age of onset between 15 and 29 years.
- It has been estimated that 24–31 per cent of people with BN have a previous diagnosis of AN.
- Biological risk factors include genetics and a history of mental illness in the family, perinatal factors, puberty, and premorbid weight.

- Psychological risk factors include impulsivity, internalisation of the thin ideal, low self-esteem and low mood and difficulty regulating emotions.
- Sociocultural risk factors include weight-related teasing, stressful life events, and a history of a critical home life.
- The key feature of BN is the presence of the binge-purge cycle. During binge eating, someone will eat a large volume of food in a short space of time with an associated feeling of being out of control.
- Types of purging behaviours include self-induced vomiting, fasting for prolonged periods, abuse of medication (e.g. diuretics and laxatives), and excessive exercise.
- People with BN have an increased risk of experiencing self-harm and suicidal thoughts, and are eight times more likely than the general population to die by suicide.
- The initial assessment of BN is often done by a GP and consists of a history (a discussion with the person to understand their current symptoms, duration of illness, binge and purging behaviours) followed by an examination to look for any complications which may have developed.
- Hypokalaemia (low potassium) may develop due to purging behaviours. There may be no outward signs of this, but it can be fatal due to its effects on the heart rhythm.
- Treatment consists of establishing a normal eating pattern, the cessation of binge eating and purging, and addressing underlying thoughts which drive the disorder. This may be through self-directed self-help or eating disorder specialists.
- Recovery from BN is always possible, and the outcome is better in adolescents.

REFERENCES

American Psychiatric Association. (2013). *Diagnostic and statistical manual of mental disorders: DSM-5*, 5th edition. Washington, DC: American Psychiatric Publishing.

Bulik, C., Blake, L., & Austin, J. (2019). Genetics of eating disorders: what the clinician needs to know. *Psychiatr Clin North Am*, 2019 Mar; 42(1), 59–73. doi 10.1016/j.psc.2018.10.007.

Castillo, M., & Weiselberg, E. (2017). Bulimia nervosa/purging disorder. *Current Problems in Pediatric and Adolescent Health Care*, 47(4), 85–94. https://doi.org/10.1016/j.cppeds.2017.02.004.

Eneva, K. T., Murray, S., O'Garro-Moore, J., Yiu, A., Alloy, L. B., Avena, N. M., & Chen, E. Y. (2017). Reward and punishment sensitivity and disordered eating behaviors in men and women. *Journal of Eating Disorders*, 5, art. 6. https://doi.org/10.1186/s40337-017-0138-2.

Favaro, A., Tenconi, E., & Santonastaso, P. (2006). Perinatal factors and the risk of developing anorexia nervosa and bulimia nervosa. *Archives of General Psychiatry*, 63(1), 82–88.

Gibson, D., Workman, C., & Mehler, P. S. (2019). Medical complications of anorexia nervosa and bulimia nervosa. *Psychiatric Clinics of North America*, 42(2), 263–274. https://doi.org/10.1016/j.psc.2019.01.009.

Gorrell, S., & Le Grange, D. (2019). Update on treatments for adolescent bulimia nervosa. *Child and Adolescent Psychiatric Clinics of North America*, 28(4), 537–547. https://doi.org/10.1016/j.chc.2019.05.002.

Hilbert, A., Pike, K. M., Goldschmidt, A. B., Wilfley, D. E., Fairburn, C. G., Dohm, F. A., ... & Striegel Weissman, R. (2014). Risk factors across the eating disorders. *Psychiatry Research*, 220(1–2), 500–506. https://doi.org/10.1016/j.psychres.2014.05.054.

Himmerich, H., Bentley, J., Kan, C., & Treasure, J. (2019). Genetic risk factors for eating disorders: an update and insights into pathophysiology. *Therapeutic Advances in Psychopharmacology*, 9. https://doi.org/10.1177/2045125318814734.

National Institute for Health and Care Excellence. (2017). *Eating disorders: recognition and treatment*. NICE guideline [NG69]. London: NICE. www.nice.org.uk/guidance/ng69/chapter/Recommendations.

Nitsch, A., Dlugosz, H., Gibson, D., & Mehler, P. S. (2021). Medical complications of bulimia nervosa. *Cleveland Clinic Journal of Medicine*, 88(6), 333–343. https://doi.org/10.3949/ccjm.88a.20168.

Pollard, N. J. (2019). The ABCDE tool for spotting the early signs of an eating disorder. *The Family Files*, 4. FamilyMentalWealth.com/FamilyFiles.

Stice, E., Gau, J. M., Rohde, P., & Shaw, H. (2017). Risk factors that predict future onset of each DSM-5 eating disorder: predictive specificity in high-risk adolescent females. *Journal of Abnormal Psychology*, 126(1), 38–51. https://doi.org/10.1037/abn0000219.

van Eeden, A. E., van Hoeken, D., & Hoek, H. W. (2021). Incidence, prevalence and mortality of anorexia nervosa and bulimia nervosa. *Current Opinion in Psychiatry*, 34(6), 515–524. https://doi.org/10.1097/YCO.0000000000000739.

Wade, T. D. (2019). Recent research on bulimia nervosa. *Psychiatric Clinics of North America*, 42(1), 21–32. https://doi.org/10.1016/j.psc.2018.10.002.

Westmoreland, P., Krantz, M. J., & Mehler, P. S. (2016). Medical complications of anorexia nervosa and bulimia. *American Journal of Medicine*, 129(1), 30–37. https://doi.org/10.1016/j.amjmed.2015.06.031.

World Health Organization. (2022). *ICD-11: international classification of diseases*, 11th revision. https://icd.who.int/.

Zerwas, S., Larsen, J. T., Petersen, L., Thornton, L. M., Quaranta, M., Koch S.V., ... & Bulik, C. M. (2017). Eating disorders, autoimmune, and autoinflammatory disease. *Pediatrics*, 140(6), e20162089. doi:10.1542/peds.2016-2089.

6

BINGE EATING DISORDER

Dr Elizabeth McNaught

BACKGROUND

Binge eating disorder (BED) is one of the most common eating disorders, but least understood. This is in part due to a lack of recognition, and the shame, embarrassment, and stigma people feel. It was only formally recognised as an eating disorder, in its own right, when it was included in 2013 in the DSM-5 (*Diagnostic and Statistical Manual of Mental Disorders*). BED is more common in females than males, but the sex distribution is less skewed and more balanced than anorexia nervosa (AN) and bulimia nervosa (BN), with an estimated female:male ratio of 6:4 (Guerdjikova et al., 2017), and a frequent crossover has been recognised with BN. Onset is often later in life, during early adulthood, but it may be seen in late adolescents, and is found to have a longer duration of illness (Brownley et al., 2016). BED can affect anyone regardless of their age, gender, ethnicity, and sexuality, and has an estimated lifetime prevalence of 1.9 per cent in women and 0.3 per cent in men (NICE, 2019). It has been suggested that BED is often underdiagnosed and undertreated, so these figures may underrepresent the true impact of the disorder.

> My experience is probably not what most people think of when they hear "eating disorder". This is because I am obese, and I don't look as though I struggle to eat. My struggle has been to stop overeating.
>
> Sophie Reindorp

DOI: 10.4324/9781003342762-6

Understanding the risk factors and how BED develops can be considered through the biopsychosocial model, looking at the role of biological, psychological, and sociocultural elements.

BIOLOGICAL

There has been recent research into the genetic basis for BED, with twin-based studies demonstrating a heritability estimate between 0.39 and 0.45 (Bulik et al., 2019). In addition, there is thought to be significant genetic correlation between BED and BN and, independently, with alcohol dependence (Bulik et al., 2019). The presence of a family history of BED increases the risk, as does a family history or personal history of obesity (Agüera et al., 2021).

Other biological risk factors include the role of puberty, as oestrogen has been suggested to have an effect on genetically vulnerable females (Guerdjikova et al., 2017).

PSYCHOLOGICAL

Psychological risk factors describe elements of who we are as people and our personality. Many different psychological factors have been identified as influencing the development of BED. These include negative affectivity (the tendency to experience negative emotions), perfectionism (the strong desire to achieve, self-set, perfect standards), substance abuse, and body dissatisfaction (being unhappy with how one's body looks) (Hilbert, 2019). In addition, low self-esteem and perceived pressure to be thin have also been linked (Agüera et al., 2021).

BED has also been associated with high levels of impulsiveness, neuroticism, and sensation seeking behaviour (Agüera et al., 2021). The presence of comorbid mental illness has also been identified as a risk factor.

SOCIOCULTURAL

Sociocultural risk factors describe the influences of the world around us. One commonly discussed risk factor is dieting, which (due to food restriction) is a well-recognised trigger for overeating (Agüera et al., 2021). In addition, internalisation and overvaluation of the "thin ideal", with a perceived pressure to be thin, has also been discussed as a risk factor (Hilbert, 2019).

Other sociocultural risk factors include: having a sedentary life-style and preference for high-calorie foods (Agüera et al., 2021), family weight concerns, parenting conflict and family conflict (Hilbert, 2019), severe childhood obesity and family history of overeating (Hilbert et al., 2014), eating in absence of hunger (Bohon, 2019), weight-based teasing, family overeating, family mental illness, and traumatic life events (Agüera, 2021).

> I'm not sure I can remember a time when I wasn't preoccupied by food, or when I didn't use it to cope. I have clear memories of myself at primary school age, stealing food from the kitchen and taking it upstairs to binge on in secret.
>
> Sharon Miklosova

PRESENTATION

BED is characterised by episodes of binge eating in the absence of any compensatory behaviours. People with BED may have a background of tending to overeat and have variable eating patterns (they may eat more at meals or snack more; Hilbert, 2019), or a history of frequent dieting. Episodes are often triggered by interpersonal distress, difficulty in managing emotions, and negative affect.

> I was eating for comfort, but it wasn't the true comfort of love, care, or compassion – it was a cynical sort of comfort, which was as much about harming myself as it was about filling my stomach. I knew it was bad for me and I did it anyway, even though deep down I didn't want to.
>
> Sophie Reindorp

During binge eating episodes, the key feature is a feeling of loss of control. People with BED consume large volumes of food (more than would be considered normal) over a defined period of time (usually two hours). They may eat in a rapid, uncontrolled way, eating until they are uncomfortably full. This results in feelings of distress, shame, and guilt. Episodes happen in private and may be planned or unplanned, and those with BED will often feel intense negative emotions after this, such as shame and guilt.

> I knew it was wrong, something to hide and feel ashamed of, but I'm not sure I understood why at that point. All I knew was that it was something I felt I needed to do, a compulsion, a way of dealing with all the difficult feelings I didn't want to feel, and the situations I didn't want to face. I would physically push them all down, into submission, with any food I could find.
>
> Sharon Miklosova

People with BED are often, but not always, overweight, with around half being obese (BMI ≥ 30 kg/m^2), 23 per cent being overweight (BMI 25–29.9 kg/m^2) and 20 per cent being of normal weight (BMI 18.5–24.9 kg/m^2) (Citrome, 2019). There is thought to be a correlation between the prevalence of this eating disorder and BMI, with the prevalence increasing with increasing BMI (Agüera et al., 2021). When people present to health care professionals, excessive focus may be placed on the obesity, and the eating disorder may not be addressed (Guerdjikova et al., 2017).

> Outside of the eating disorder world, every health care professional will tell you that you need to lose weight. Luckily, my dietitian understood how weight management and eating disorder care works in the NHS.
>
> Sophie Reindorp

> It is important to separate BED from obesity, with the former causing more significant functional impairment, reduced quality of life, and distress.
>
> (Citrome, 2019)

Due to the shame and stigma felt, people will often be reluctant to disclose what is happening, in addition, they may be unaware of it as an eating disorder. The ABCDE model can be used to help understand and look out for key features (Pollard, 2019). Note that exercise doesn't appear to be an indicator of BED, so it has been left off this list.

> I learned to eat a lot of food in secret and live with shame, guilt, and fear of discovery. It was a pattern that continued into adulthood. I ate large amounts of food and hid it from those closest to me.
>
> Sophie Reindorp

- A – Absence
  Binge eating often occurs in private. They may have hidden food, to be accessed in a binge, and may become socially withdrawn.
- B – Body
  Changes in their body shape and weight with weight gain is common. This is due to calorie excess. They may have significant weight and shape concerns.
- C – Control
  During binge eating episodes, they feel out of control over what they are eating, feeling that they can't stop eating after the binge has started. They may eat in a rapid and mechanical way, not tasting the food.
- D – Diet
  They may plan a binge and buy foods for that, storing them in secret locations, or binges may happen spontaneously. During these episodes, they may eat foods that are high in calories and easy to consume. Outside of a binge eating episode, they may have chaotic eating habits.

DIAGNOSIS

Doctors make a diagnosis of BED based on the DSM-5 (*Diagnostic and Statistical Manual of Mental Disorders*) and/or ICD-11 (*International Classification of Diseases*) (American Psychiatric Association, 2013; World Health Organization, 2022).

Diagnostic features drawn from these are:

- Recurrent episodes of binge eating behaviours.
  - These are episodes where someone will eat a large volume of food which is more than most people would eat.
  - During these episodes people feel out of control and unable to stop or limit what they are eating.
  - These overeating episodes often occur during a short period of time – typically two hours.

- These episodes are associated with eating quicker than they usually do, eating until they are uncomfortably full, eating even when they don't feel hungry, a desire to eat alone to avoid others seeing, and feelings of guilt and shame about their actions.
- Binge eating causes significant distress, with associated negative emotions.
- Binge eating causes significant impairment in someone's ability to function in everyday life.
- There is an absence of any compensatory behaviours.
- The disordered eating does not occur during a current presentation of AN or BN or due to another mental health or medical condition.

While concerns over weight and shape are not part of the diagnostic criteria, their presence is common and related to greater eating disorder symptoms and a worse outcome (Agüera et al., 2021).

> Although it was a relief to find out that my eating behaviours, and the distress I'd experienced because of it, weren't because I was an inherently bad person, it took a while for me to stop doubting that the diagnosis was real and true for me.
>
> Anny Johnson

It can be a challenge to differentiate BED with obesity from obesity on its own. The former is often associated with greater levels of comorbid mental illness and higher levels of overvaluation of body shape and weight.

It is thought that around four out of five people with BED have at least one other mental illness (Guerdjikova et al., 2017), with multiple comorbidities being common and higher comorbidity rates being linked to childhood development (Agüera et al., 2021). The most common comorbid mental illnesses are mood and anxiety disorders. Others include personality disorders (particularly emotionally unstable personality disorder), impulse control disorders, and alcohol and substance misuse.

CONSULTATION WITH A DOCTOR

Due to the lack of awareness around BED as an eating disorder, and the shame and stigma felt by people living with it, they will often be reluctant to disclose their symptoms to a health care professional.

In addition, health care professionals will often place greater emphasis on weight and obesity management than on discovering the underlying eating pathology.

> Over the decades, I became very good at hiding what was going on, and I never looked like the stereotype of someone with an eating disorder, so no one ever guessed. I did mention my struggle with food to doctors a couple of times, but was always given weight loss advice.
> Sharon Miklosova

When someone presents to a health care professional, this will often be their GP, whose assessment will consist of two parts: gaining a history and conducting a physical assessment.

HISTORY

"Taking a history" is the process whereby the doctor talks to the patient and gathers information. The doctor will often ask about current symptoms. Someone with BED may feel reluctant to disclose what they have been eating and how they have been feeling about it, and it may take them multiple appointments to develop the confidence in the doctor–patient relationship to begin to disclose.

> My GP was a black woman, which made it easier to speak openly – I felt safe speaking to someone who looked like me. She was everything you'd expect a good GP to be: compassionate, kind, empathetic, and understanding, but most of all she was a good listener.
> Anny Johnson

The doctor will often want to know what the person with BED is eating, during both their day-to-day life and the binge eating episodes. They will want to find out how this is making them feel both during a binge eating episode and after, and how often these events are happening. To make a diagnosis, the doctor will need to ask and exclude the presence of any compensatory behaviours. They may want to discover how long this has been going on and when it started, and the impact it is having on the person's day-to-day life. In addition, they will often screen for any comorbid mental illness, especially thoughts of self-harm or suicide.

It was during that phone call, and answering questions, when I realised how serious my eating habits were and the first time I became aware that I demonstrated the symptoms of an eating disorder. My response was to laugh, but that was because I couldn't believe someone like me, at my age, could have an eating disorder.

Anny Johnson

ASSESSMENT

A doctor may decide to conduct a physical assessment to look for any complications. This may be through a physical examination, checking blood pressure and heart rate and measuring height and weight to calculate BMI. Due to the strong link between BED and obesity and the well-recognised association between obesity and physical complications, the doctor may also choose to do some blood tests to check for any medical comorbidities (e.g. type 2 diabetes) they may have developed.

Physical complications from binge eating and subsequent weight gain include the following (Citrome, 2019; Guerdjikova et al., 2017; Hilbert, 2019; Wassenaar et al., 2019):

- Neurological
  - Idiopathic intercranial hypertension (a build-up of pressure around the brain which may result in headaches).
- Sleep
  - Disrupted sleep and obstructive sleep apnoea (repeated episodes of stopping breathing in the night, often due to an obstruction of the airway).
- Cardiovascular
  - Hypertension (raised blood pressure).
  - Dyslipidaemia (unhealthy levels of fats in the bloodstream).
  - Cardiovascular disease.
- Gastrointestinal
  - Gastric reflux (reflux of stomach acid into the oesophagus).
  - Bloating and abdominal pain.
  - Stomach ulcers (sores which develop in the lining of the stomach, often causing abdominal pain).
  - They may notice a change in their bowel habits, with constipation or diarrhoea.
  - Irritable bowel syndrome.

- Hepatobiliary
  - Non-alcoholic fatty liver disease (NAFLD). Obesity increases the risk of developing NAFLD. There are three stages of this condition – steatosis (fatty infiltration to the liver), steato-hepatitis (inflammation of the liver with fatty infiltration), and cirrhosis (irreversible scarring of the liver).
- Reproductive health
  - Binge eating behaviour has been linked to changes in periods (a reduction or stopping of periods and premenstrual dysphoric disorder).
  - Polycystic ovarian syndrome (PCOS) has been linked to BED.
  - Increased risk of miscarriage.
  - There have also been links with pregnancy complications, including having larger babies and longer labours.
- Metabolic
  - Type 2 diabetes.
  - Metabolic syndrome (a collection of conditions which increase the risk of cardiovascular disease).
  - Nutritional disturbance. Due to overconsumption of certain foods (typically high-fat and sugary foods), people may have a reduced intake of more nutritious food, and are at risk of developing nutritional deficiencies. This may be further perpetuated if they have bariatric surgery.
- Cancer
  - Obesity is well recognised as a risk factor for multiple different cancers.

POTENTIAL FOR BLIND SPOTS, MISDIAGNOSES, AND BIASES

When someone is assessed for BED, the doctor will often consider alternative "differential" diagnoses – other conditions which may explain the symptoms they are presenting with. These may include obesity without an underlying eating disorder, problems with the gastrointestinal system, metabolic conditions (e.g. hypothyroidism and Cushing's syndrome), reproductive system disorders (e.g. PCOS), and effects of medication or other mental illnesses (e.g. BN, depression, night eating syndrome).

A common misconception held by the general public and health care professionals is that the behaviour is due to poor self-control and a lack of willpower. While during an episode of binge eating people often report feeling "out of control", that is a symptom of the disorder more than a cause. The disorder is driven by deep-seated psychological, emotional, and biological processes.

In addition, people will often wish to focus on weight loss as part of their treatment. However, while establishing a healthy weight is important to prevent physical complications developing it should not be seen as a treatment in itself.

> As with BN, it is important to note a difference between subjective and objective binge eating. With subjective binge eating, there is a perception of having overeaten, when they have consumed what would be considered "normal" in that setting and time frame, and objective binge eating being the consumption of a large volume of food, more than most well people would consume.

TREATMENT

Treatment for BED should ideally be provided by a multidisciplinary team (MDT), with treatment focusing on reducing episodes of binge eating, and addressing and challenging eating disorder thoughts, behaviours and symptoms. For many people living with BED, weight loss will be high on their priority list. However, the guidance is not to have weight loss as a target, and instead to establish a regular eating pattern to reduce binge eating episodes. In reducing these episodes weight loss may occur concurrently.

> I'd learned that recovery wasn't the same as losing weight and I had to make peace with that in order to heal my mind.
>
> Anny Johnson

The role of medication has been discussed, with studies looking at the effects of a range of medicines, including antidepressants, antiepileptic medication (specifically a medication called topiramate), weight loss medication (orlistat), and the central nervous system stimulant Lisdexamfetamine. The latter is the only medication which has received Food and Drug Administration (FDA) approval for binge eating disorder. Some studies have shown that it results in a reduction in eating disorder symptoms and weight loss, but long-term outcomes are less clear, and it also has the potential for significant adverse effects, abuse, and dependence.

Other treatments that have been studied include the effect of behavioural weight loss treatments and bariatric surgery. Currently the NICE (National Institute for Health and Care Excellence) guidelines focus on psychological treatments, advising that medication should not be used as a sole treatment.

Psychological treatment may not result in weight loss, but has been shown to reduce eating disorder behaviours. NICE sets out treatment guidelines, and the following section is adapted from this (NICE, 2017).

TALKING THERAPY

For adults and children, the first-line treatment is a BED-focused guided self-help programme. This is a self-directed treatment given via self-help materials based on a cognitive behavioural therapy (CBT) method. This should be accompanied by brief supportive sessions.

If this treatment is ineffective, contraindicated, or unacceptable, then the next step would be treatment with group eating-disorder-focused CBT (CBT-ED). This consists of weekly sessions where there is a focus on education about the disorder and supporting the people to engage in self-monitoring of thoughts and behaviours at home. The person in treatment will be asked to track their food intake at home and identify triggers for binge eating. This treatment may also support people to challenge negative beliefs about their body and develop skills and techniques to prevent relapse.

> It's no exaggeration when I say that my 12-week group therapy was a lifesaver. Not only did I learn life tools and skills that helped me to feel more confident about managing my life and my emotions, but being in a group with other people who completely understood and were living this eating disorder too was comforting. The shame began to reduce and I didn't feel as alone as I had before.
>
> Anny Johnson

If both treatments are ineffective or not usable, then the third-line treatment is to offer individual CBT. This is provided on a one-to-one basis. During treatment, the person with BED will be supported in understanding more about why their eating disorder has developed and what is maintaining it. They will be helped to understand how different patterns of eating and emotions affect their eating, and iden-tify triggers for binge eating episodes. They will then be supported in using therapies to develop skills to overcome this. During this treatment, people will be encouraged to engage in self-monitoring of their food intake, behaviours, and emotions, and may have their weight monitored.

During all treatments, the person should be advised to adhere to a "normal" regular eating pattern.

Further information about treatment can be found in chapter 11.

OUTCOMES

Recovery is always possible, though people may show a relapsing and remitting picture. It has been estimated that around 70 to 80 per cent of people with BED achieve recovery (NICE, 2019). Once treatment is established, the presence of a rapid reduction in binge eating in the first four weeks is a positive indicator for the long-term outcome (Hilbert, 2019).

SUMMARY

- Binge eating disorder (BED) is one of the more common eating disorders and tends to have an onset in early adulthood.
- A frequent crossover has been recognised between BED and bulimia nervosa (BN).
- Biological risk factors include genetics, a family history of BED and obesity, and puberty.
- Psychological risk factors include negative affectivity, perfection-ism, impulsiveness, and sensation-seeking behaviour.
- Sociocultural risk factors include dieting, a sedentary lifestyle, and conflict in the home.
- People with BED are often, but not always, overweight and there is thought to be a positive correlation between the prevalence of BED and BMI.
- The key features of BED are episodes of binge eating (where people eat large volumes of food in a short period of time, asso-ciated with the feeling of being out of control), in the absence of any purging behaviour.
- BED is commonly comorbid with other mental illnesses, with four out of five people thought to have at least one psychiatric comorbidity.

- The initial assessment of BED is often carried out by a GP and consists of a history (a discussion with the person to understand their current symptoms, duration of illness, and food intake), followed by an examination to look for any complications which may have developed.

- A common misconception around BED is that the behaviour is due to poor self-control and a lack of willpower, but this is not the case.

- Treatment of BED is focused on addressing the underlying thoughts and beliefs which drive the behaviour, and establishing a regular eating pattern. People will often want to engage in weight loss behaviour, but this might be counterproductive to recovery.

- 70 to 80 per cent of people with BED achieve recovery.

REFERENCES

Agüera, Z., Lozano-Madrid, M., Mallorquí-Bagué, N., Jiménez-Murcia, S., Menchón, J. M., & Fernández-Aranda, F. (2021). A review of binge eating disorder and obesity. *Neuropsychiatrie: Klinik, Diagnostik, Therapie und Rehabilitation: Organ der Gesellschaft Osterreichischer Nervenarzte und Psychiater*, 35(2), 57–67. https://doi.org/10.1007/s40211-020-00346-w.

American Psychiatric Association. (2013). *Diagnostic and statistical manual of mental disorders: DSM-5*, 5th edition. Washington, DC: American Psychiatric Publishing.

Bohon, C. (2019). Binge eating disorder in children and adolescents. *Child and Adolescent Psychiatric Clinics*, 28(4), 549–555. https://doi.org/10.1016/j.chc.2019.05.003.

Brownley, K. A., Berkman, N. D., Peat, C. M., Lohr, K. N., Cullen, K. E., Bann, C. M., & Bulik, C. M. (2016). Binge-eating disorder in adults: a systematic review and meta-analysis. *Annals of Internal Medicine*, 165(6), 409–420. https://doi.org/10.7326/M15-2455.

Bulik, C., Blake, L., & Austin, J. (2019). Genetics of eating disorders: what the clinician needs to know. *Psychiatric Clinics of North America*, 42(1), 59–73. doi 10.1016/j.psc.2018.10.007.

Citrome, L. (2019). Binge eating disorder revisited: what's new, what's different, what's next. *CNS Spectrums*, 24(S1), 4–13. https://doi.org/10.1017/S1092852919001032.

Guerdjikova, A. I., Mori, N., Casuto, L. S., & McElroy, S. L. (2017). Binge eating disorder. *Psychiatric Clinics of North America*, 40(2), 255–266. https://doi.org/10.1016/j.psc.2017.01.003.

Hilbert, A. (2019). Binge-eating disorder. *Psychiatric Clinics of North America*, 42(1), 33–43. https://doi.org/10.1016/j.psc.2018.10.011.

Hilbert, A., Pike, K. M., Goldschmidt, A. B., Wilfley, D. E., Fairburn, C. G., Dohm, F. A. …, & Striegel Weissman, R. (2014). Risk factors across the eating disorders. *Psychiatry Research*, 220(1–2), 500–506. https://doi.org/10.1016/j.psychres.2014.05.054.

National Institute for Health and Care Excellence. (2017). *Eating disorders: recognition and treatment.* NICE guideline [NG69]. London: NICE. www.nice.org.uk/guidance/ng69/chapter/Recommendations.

National Institute for Health and Care Excellence. (2019). Eating disorders. Clinical Knowledge Summaries (CKS): Health topics A to Z. https://cks.nice.org.uk/topics/eating-disorders/.

Pollard, N. J. (2019). The ABCDE tool for spotting the early signs of an eating disorder. *The Family Files*, 4. FamilyMentalWealth.com/FamilyFiles.

Wassenaar, E., Friedman, J., & Mehler, P. S. (2019). Medical complications of binge eating disorder. *Psychiatric Clinics of North America*, 42(2), 275–286. https://doi.org/10.1016/j.psc.2019.01.010.

World Health Organization. (2022). *ICD-11: international classification of diseases, 11th revision).* https://icd.who.int/.

7

OTHER SPECIFIED FEEDING OR EATING DISORDER

Dr Elizabeth McNaught

BACKGROUND

Other specified feeding or eating disorder (often shortened to "OSFED") was introduced to the DSM-5 (*Diagnostic and Statistical Manual of Mental Disorders*) in 2013 and (alongside unspecified feeding or eating disorder; UFED) replaces the category of eating disorder not otherwise specified (EDNOS) (American Psychiatric Association, 2013). OSFED is unique to the DSM-5, with the ICD-11 (*International Classification of Diseases*) listing a residual category, other specified feeding or eating disorders (OSFED; World Health Organisation, 2022).

OSFED is the most common eating disorder (NICE, 2019) and comprises a heterogenous group of five different eating pathologies:

- atypical anorexia nervosa
- bulimia nervosa (of low frequency and/or limited duration)
- binge eating disorder (of low frequency and/or limited duration)
- purging disorder
- night eating syndrome.

These subcategories are all characterised by dysfunctional eating, which has a significant impact on people's ability to function in everyday life and causes significant distress. The presentations do not meet the threshold for previously discussed eating disorders, however. For example, this may be due to an absence of low body weight or behaviour not occurring frequently enough (subthreshold behaviour frequency). The risk factors and personality traits for each condition are similar to the condition they represent, and people living

DOI: 10.4324/9781003342762-7

with OSFED often experience high levels of overevaluation of their weight and shape (Jenkins et al., 2021).

Due to the presence of fewer symptoms or people being of higher weight, many might view OSFED as a less severe eating disorder. Nevertheless, there is minimal difference in the severity of symptoms experienced and treatment outcomes compared to other eating disorders (Withnell et al., 2022), and complications which may develop are similar to those seen in the condition they closely represent.

> Despite the purging, restricting, and hating the way I looked, weight always seemed to be a significant factor: "Well, you look fine" and "Your BMI isn't low enough" is something I had become so used to hearing.
> Anjali Heer

> Getting a letter to say that I wasn't worth helping because I was "too healthy" when I was drinking to excess and making myself sick up to ten times a day was one of the most invalidating experiences of my entire life. I genuinely felt there was no point in going on.
> Christina Taylor

OSFED is commonly comorbid with other mental health conditions, including self-harming behaviour and suicidal thoughts (Withnell et al., 2022). Not much is known about treatment outcomes and prognosis, and this varies depending on the symptoms experienced and complications developed. It is thought that people living with OSFED often have a low motivation to make a change (Riesco et al., 2018). NICE (National Institute for Health and Care Excellence, 2019) recommends that treatment is given as per the eating disorder that the presentation most closely represents and there is some evidence for the benefit of transdiagnostic treatment models, including enhanced cognitive behavioural therapy (CBT-E) (Withnell et al., 2022).

> At the time, I was diagnosed with clinical depression and severe anxiety. So, to cope with my self-hatred, I would take it out on my body. This included not allowing myself to eat, throwing up constantly, being extremely self-critical over the way I looked, and self-harm.
> Anjali Heer

As well as my eating disorder, I was struggling a lot with depression, self-harm and suicide ideation. I didn't really care about myself or my health.

Jess Sharman

I started using alcohol to self-medicate and drank excessively to ease my anxiety around food ... I also started using drugs.

Christina Taylor

ATYPICAL ANOREXIA NERVOSA

Atypical anorexia is defined as the presence of restrictive eating resulting in weight loss, engagement in behaviours aimed to prevent weight gain, a fear of weight gain or behaviour to prevent weight gain, and an overevaluation of body weight and shape. This presentation lacks a significantly low body weight, and it is this which separates it from anorexia nervosa (AN) (American Psychiatric Association, 2013).

People living with atypical anorexia will often have been overweight prior to the onset of their eating disorder (it has been estimated that 70 per cent of people were premorbidly obese; Sawyer et al., 2016). They often experience rapid weight loss, which in the context of a previously raised BMI may be encouraged by family, friends, and society around them, which results in the potential for a delay in diagnosis or misdiagnosis.

I think my disordered eating began aged 9 – I started eating in secret after my mum had a breakdown ... I carried on doing this until I was 13 – I gained significant amounts of weight and was bullied ... I lost some weight on a family holiday and remember the girls at school treating me more positively and being less cruel about how I looked. Taking pride in the compliments I received about my weight loss, I resolved to change myself, wrote a list of things I wanted to be different, and a diet and exercise regime was on this. My eating disorder developed extremely quickly.

Christina Taylor

> Every weight loss goal I reached, I set myself a new one. I exercised excessively, irrespective of where I was. My dad worked away a lot overseas and my mum was a teacher who was always really busy.
>
> Christina Taylor

Through the course of the disorder, they may experience significant weight loss, which can result in them being underweight, of normal weight, or overweight. Regardless of weight, this restrictive behaviour can lead to malnourishment, similar to that seen in AN (Nagata et al., 2018), and physical complications similar to those seen in AN – for example, electrolyte abnormalities and bradycardia (a low heart rate) (Moskowitz & Weiselberg, 2017).

It has been suggested that people with atypical anorexia have the same or a worse level of psychological symptoms (for example, concern about body shape and weight) compared to those with AN (Walsh et al., 2023).

The assessment and treatment of atypical anorexia is very similar to that of AN, with a focus on reversing malnutrition (weight gain may be required regardless of presenting weight), establishing structured eating patterns and addressing the underlying thought processes which establish and maintain the disorder.

BULIMIA NERVOSA (OF LOW FREQUENCY AND/ OR LIMITED DURATION)

Bulimia nervosa (of low frequency and/or limited duration) is defined as the presence of dysfunctional eating, presenting with episodes of binge eating followed by purging (this may be through self-induced vomiting, excessive exercise, fasting, or medication abuse such as laxatives) which has a significant impact on life and functioning. These episodes occur less than once a week and/or for less than three months, whereas in bulimia nervosa (BN) behaviour occurs at least once a week for three months (American Psychiatric Association, 2013).

BINGE EATING DISORDER (OF LOW FREQUENCY AND/OR LIMITED DURATION)

Binge eating disorder (of low frequency and/or limited duration) is defined as the presence of dysfunctional eating, presenting with episodes of binge eating, in the absence of purging behaviours, which has a significant impact on life and functioning. These episodes occur less than once a week and/or for less than three months, whereas in binge eating disorder (BED) behaviour occurs at least once a week for three months (American Psychiatric Association, 2013).

PURGING DISORDER

Purging disorder used to be thought of as part of BN, but is now recognised as a condition in its own right. It is defined as the presence of purging behaviour (for example, self-induced vomiting, laxative or medication abuse, fasting, or excessive exercise) as a method to change their body shape or weight (American Psychiatric Association, 2013). People will often experience an improvement in their negative thoughts and emotions after purging (Castillo et al., 2017), which further reinforces the behaviour. Purging occurs in the absence of any binge eating and this differentiates it from BN. In addition, people are often of normal weight. If they were of low body weight, then this presentation may be considered under AN.

> The more I felt I was being forced to eat at home, the more I felt I needed to be creative about how to avoid it. That's when the purging started.
> Cara Lisette

Those with purging disorder are at risk of developing similar complications to those seen in BN (with varying complications, depending on the purging technique used), including electrolyte imbalances (which may lead to cardiac arrhythmias), oesophageal tears, and changes in their bowel habit after chronic laxative abuse. It may also present with similar psychiatric comorbidities to other eating disorders. Purging disorder is thought to have a higher mortality than BN (Lydecker et al., 2018).

> I cannot help feeling frustrated and deeply disappointed that my eating disorder has only ever been taken seriously when it has met criteria for anorexia, despite the danger and distress that come with frequent purging behaviours. Most people with purging disorder will not become underweight, but that doesn't mean they are at a healthy weight for their body, and it doesn't mean they aren't causing harm to themselves.
> Cara Lisette

The treatment is often similar to that of BN. Not much is known of the outcomes, but it has been suggested that some may go on to develop BN or BED (Keel, 2019).

> I was referred back to the eating disorders service again and diagnosed with purging disorder – the first time in 15 years of these difficulties that it had been given its own name. I felt reassured by that. If this is now considered a diagnosis in and of itself, that must mean there was some help available for me?
>
> Cara Lisette

NIGHT EATING SYNDROME

Night eating syndrome was first described in 1955, and recognised as an eating disorder under the OSFED category in the DSM-5 in 2013 (American Psychiatric Association, 2013).

Night eating syndrome is characterised by repeated episodes of eating food in the night, which results in significant distress and impairment in functioning, and isn't better explained by another eating disorder or medical or psychiatric condition. Eating behaviour occurs any time after the evening meal and before waking, and may happen prior to any sleep or after waking from sleep in the night, so people then often have a lack of appetite in the mornings. During the eating episodes, people are aware and conscious of their behaviour. It is important to separate night eating syndrome from sleep-related eating disorder (the latter also presenting with eating in the night, but this happens in the context of partial to absent consciousness, often happening on the transition from sleep to wake).

Night eating syndrome often occurs in people who are obese (Kaur et al., 2022) and is more common in women than men. It is thought that low mood in the evenings is a driving factor for eating behaviours, and eating can act to placate these emotions. In addition, eating in the evenings means that people can often hide this from other people.

It is commonly comorbid with other eating disorders, particularly those with binge-eating aspects (BN and BED) and other mental health conditions, including depression and low self-esteem. It acts as a risk factor for obesity and, when night eating syndrome and obesity are comorbid, the prognosis for weight loss is felt to be poor (Kaur et al., 2022).

SUMMARY

- Other specified feeding or eating disorder (OSFED) is the most common eating disorder.
- OSFED comprises a heterogenous group of five different eating pathologies, all characterised by dysfunctional eating that has a significant impact on life and functioning.
- Many view OSFED as a less severe eating disorder. However, there is minimal difference in the severity of symptoms experienced compared to the eating disorder they most closely represent.
- OSFED is commonly comorbid with other mental health conditions.
- NICE recommends that treatment should be provided as per the eating disorder the presentation most closely represents.
- Atypical anorexia is described as the presence of behaviour which fulfils the diagnostic criteria for anorexia nervosa (AN), except that the person is not sufficiently underweight. They often experience rapid weight loss and are at risk of malnutrition and physical complications resembling those seen in AN.
- Bulimia nervosa of low frequency and/or limited duration is the presence of binge eating and purging behaviour comparable to that seen in bulimia nervosa (BN), except that these episodes occur below the threshold for diagnosis of BN.
- Binge eating disorder of low frequency and/or limited duration is the presence of binge eating similar to that seen in binge eating disorder (BED), except that these episodes occur below the threshold for diagnosis of BN.
- Purging disorder describes the presence of purging behaviour (with a desire to alter body shape and weight) in the absence of binge eating. They are at risk of developing similar complications to those seen in BN.
- Night eating syndrome describes the presence of repeated episodes of eating in the night (any time after the evening meal, and it may happen before or after sleep), in full consciousness. Often people are obese, and the disorder is commonly comorbid with other eating disorders.

REFERENCES

American Psychiatric Association. (2013). *Diagnostic and statistical manual of mental disorders: DSM-5*, 5th edition. Washington, DC: American Psychiatric Publishing.

Castillo, M., & Weiselberg, E. (2017). Bulimia nervosa/purging disorder. *Current Problems in Pediatric and Adolescent Health Care*, 47(4), 85–94. https://doi.org/10.1016/j.cppeds.2017.02.004.

Fairweather-Schmidt, A. K., & Wade, T. D. (2014). DSM-5 eating disorders and other specified eating and feeding disorders: is there a meaningful differentiation? *International Journal of Eating Disorders*, 47(5), 524–533. https://doi.org/10.1002/eat.22257.

Jenkins, Z. M., Mancuso, S. G., Phillipou, A., & Castle, D. J. (2021). What is OSFED? The predicament of classifying "other" eating disorders. *British Journal of Psychiatry Open*, 7(5), e147. https://doi.org/10.1192/bjo.2021.985

Kaur, J., Dang, A. B., Gan, J., An, Z., & Krug, I. (2022). Night eating syndrome in patients with obesity and binge eating disorder: a systematic review. *Frontiers in Psychology*, 12, 766827. https://doi.org/10.3389/fpsyg.2021.766827.

Keel, P. K. (2019). Purging disorder: recent advances and future challenges. *Current Opinion in Psychiatry*, 32(6), 518–524. https://doi.org/10.1097/YCO.0000000000000541.

Lydecker, J. A., Shea, M., & Grilo, C. M. (2018). Driven exercise in the absence of binge eating: implications for purging disorder. *International Journal of Eating Disorders*, 51(2), 139–145. https://doi.org/10.1002/eat.22811.

Moskowitz, L., & Weiselberg, E. (2017). Anorexia nervosa/atypical anorexia nervosa. *Current Problems in Pediatric and Adolescent Health Care*, 47(4), 70–84. https://doi.org/10.1016/j.cppeds.2017.02.003.

Nagata, J. M., Garber, A. K., & Buckelew, S. M. (2018). Weight restoration in atypical anorexia nervosa: a clinical conundrum. *International Journal of Eating Disorders*, 51(11), 1290–1293. https://doi.org/10.1002/eat.22953.

National Institute for Health and Care Excellence. (2019). Eating disorders. Clinical Knowledge Summaries (CKS): Health topics A to Z. https://cks.nice.org.uk/topics/eating-disorders/.

Riesco, N., Agüera, Z., Granero, R., Jiménez-Murcia, S., Menchón, J. M., & Fernández-Aranda, F. (2018). Other Specified Feeding or Eating Disorders (OSFED): clinical heterogeneity and cognitive-behavioral therapy outcome. *European Psychiatry: The Journal of the Association of European Psychiatrists*, 54, 109–116. https://doi.org/10.1016/j.eurpsy.2018.08.001.

Sawyer, S. M., Whitelaw, M., Le Grange, D., Yeo, M., & Hughes, E. K. (2016). Physical and psychological morbidity in adolescents with atypical anorexia nervosa. *Pediatrics*, 137(4), e20154080. https://doi.org/10.1542/peds.2015-4080.

Walsh, B. T., Hagan, K. E., & Lockwood, C. (2023). A systematic review comparing atypical anorexia nervosa and anorexia nervosa. *International Journal of Eating Disorders*, 56(4), 798–820. https://doi.org/10.1002/eat.23856.

Withnell, S. J., Kinnear, A., Masson, P., & Bodell, L. P. (2022). How different are threshold and other specified feeding and eating disorders? Comparing severity and treatment outcome. *Frontiers in psychology*, 13, 784512. https://doi.org/10.3389/fpsyg.2022.784512.

World Health Organization. (2022). *ICD-11: international classification of diseases, 11th revision*). https://icd.who.int/.

8

AVOIDANT RESTRICTIVE FOOD INTAKE DISORDER

Dr Elizabeth McNaught

BACKGROUND

Avoidant restrictive food intake disorder (ARFID) is a newly recognised eating disorder, having been formally recognised in the DSM-5 (*Diagnostic and Statistical Manual of Mental Disorders*) (American Psychiatric Association, 2013). This replaced "Feeding Disorder of Infancy or Early Childhood".

Due to its recent recognition, the true epidemiology is still unknown. However, people tend to be younger at presentation than those with anorexia nervosa (AN), bulimia nervosa (BN), and binge eating disorder (BED), with the onset often occurring in childhood. While it can occur in all ages, ethnicity, gender, and sociocultural groups, people living with ARFID are more likely to be males and have a co-existing diagnosis of neurodiversity – it has been estimated that autism spectrum disorder (ASD) is seen in 12.5 per cent of people living with ARFID (Inoue et al., 2021).

ARFID is often misdiagnosed as picky eating, but left undetected and untreated can have a profound impact on a person's life, both physically (with consequences of malnutrition) and socially (with a negative impact on their ability to function in day-to-day life and a reduction in their quality of life). While people have undoubtedly struggled in the past with this disorder, its recent formal recognition means that there is still a lot to be understood about it.

DOI: 10.4324/9781003342762-8

While we have limited knowledge as to how ARFID develops, we can start to understand risk factors through the biopsychosocial model, considering the role of biological, psychological, and socio-cultural elements.

BIOLOGICAL

It has been suggested that ARFID shows an element of heritability, with genetics playing a role in its development (Kennedy et al., 2022). In addition, if a parent has a history of anxiety or an eating disorder, this increases their child's risk. Other biological risk factors include the presence of premorbid gastrointestinal disorders such as reflux (the reflux of stomach acid into the oesophagus), vomiting, and food allergies. The presence of these medical conditions is thought to affect the process of learning how to eat different foods, and thus leads to the food restriction.

Neurodiversity, particularly ASD and attention deficit hyperactivity disorder (ADHD), is well discussed as a risk factor. It is thought that the sensory hypersensitivity seen in ASD is similar to the hypersensitivity which may drive some restriction in ARFID, and the distractibility, hyperactivity, and high levels of arousal at mealtimes in ADHD may drive the restriction, due to lack of interest in food (Coglan & Otasowie, 2019).

PSYCHOLOGICAL

Psychological risk factors describe elements of who we are as people and our personality. The presence of selective eating in early childhood has been discussed as a risk factor for ARFID, as has the presence of pre-existing psychological disorders, including anxiety disorders and obsessive compulsive disorder (OCD). Pre-existing anxiety is particularly significant when food restriction revolves around a fear of adverse events (e.g. choking, gagging, vomiting).

SOCIOCULTURAL

Sociocultural risk factors are the influences of the world around us. Parental pressure to eat, particularly in childhood, has been linked to higher levels of anxiety and picky eating and lower weight. It is thought that this effect happens because the child separates eating from hunger cues (Zimmerman & Fisher, 2017). In addition, limited exposure to different types of food has been thought to be a risk factor.

Other sociocultural risk factors include attachment disorders, poor parent and child relationships, and poor parental sensitivity to child distress (Coglan & Otasowie, 2019).

PRESENTATION

ARFID is a heterogenous group of conditions which are characterised by a restriction of food intake in variety and/or volume. This restriction is not driven by a desire to change their body shape or weight, but can result in nutritional deficiency, dependence on nutritional supplementation, and functional impairment. Note that this eating behaviour is not due to normal age-related changes, particularly the picky eating commonly seen in early childhood.

People presenting with ARFID will often have a long history of restrictive eating, with problems originating in childhood. In part, this prolonged period of illness will be due to a poor understanding (and thus detection) of the disorder. People may have sought help and been referred to gastroenterology and other medical teams instead of the mental health services. In addition, parents or carers may delay seeking help because they fear being judged for their child's eating habits.

> Throughout my childhood, I was the "pickiest" eater I knew – rivalled perhaps only by my younger sibling. My diet was so limited that my parents would pack tins of Tesco beans and sausage in the suitcases when we went on holiday, to ensure that I would have something I would eat.
> Sarah Miller

When presenting to a health care professional, this may be due to their own or their family's concerns about their eating, or due to complications such as malnutrition, dizziness, fatigue, and lethargy.

The ABCDE model can be used to help understand and look out for key features (Pollard, 2019). Note that exercise doesn't appear to be an indicator of ARFID; therefore it has been left of this list.

- A – Absence
  Avoidance of eating with people, due to embarrassment around their eating patterns or worry about exposure to certain foods.
- B – Body
  Restrictive eating resulting in malnutrition or the dependence on nutritional supplements. People may be of normal, low, or

high weight. If they are of low weight, they often recognise and acknowledge this as a negative effect. This is a key differentiating factor from AN, as their restrictive eating is not driven by a desire to change their body shape or weight.

- C – Control
  People will often control and restrict what they eat, due to feelings of anxiety on exposure to certain foods.
- D – Diet
  Avoidance of certain foods due to their look, taste, texture, or smell. The eating of or exposure to these foods will often elicit significant levels of anxiety. This food avoidance must not be due to lifestyle choices (e.g. veganism), cultural behaviours, or normal age-related changes.

> For me, strong tastes and certain textures were some of the most abhorrent sensory experiences imaginable. Pineapple was too stringy; couscous, too bitty. I could tolerate plain pasta, sometimes with a bit of cheese or baked beans, but I was extremely risk averse with other food. Textures and tastes could be so unpleasant to me that I would avoid trying new foods just in case they were disgusting. At one point, I had around ten "safe foods", and anything else was an automatic "no".
>
> Sarah Miller

DIAGNOSIS

Doctors make a diagnosis of ARFID based on the DSM-5 (*Diagnostic and Statistical Manual of Mental Disorders*) and/or the ICD-11 (*International Classification of Diseases*) (American Psychiatric Association, 2013; World Health Organisation, 2022). Diagnostic features drawn from these publications are:

- Disordered eating, resulting in a failure to meet nutritional needs. This is associated with:
  - Significant weight loss.
  - Growth failure in children.
  - Malnutrition and/or a dependence on additional feeding support to maintain nutritional status (e.g. food supplements or tube feeding).

- Negative impact on the person's physical health.
- Impairment in ability to function in their daily life, such as maintain relationships, engage in social events, and continue education or gain employment.
- This behaviour is not due to a lack of availability of food, social or cultural practices, or the presence of a medical condition or another psychiatric condition (including AN or BN).

> On days where my sensory "threshold" is close to being reached by other factors, I often resort to food supplements to get the energy in without too much sensory aversion.
>
> Sarah Miller

The DSM-5 identifies three different types of presentation of ARFID. These represent typical presentations encountered and are not mutually exclusive (American Psychiatric Association, 2013):

- A lack of interest in food
    - People may have an absence of an appetite, or food lacks its appeal; they may not enjoy eating and see this as a burden (Brigham et al., 2018). Their limited food intake only acts to further perpetuate their lack of desire to eat.
- Avoidance of food based on its sensory characteristics
    - This is the most common presentation and often presents in early childhood (Coglan & Otasowie, 2019). People have a limited food intake, due to negative sensory experiences. This is based on the food's appearance, texture, taste, and/or smell, and often results in the avoidance of foods, including vegetables, fruit, and meat (Thomas et al., 2017).
    - It has been suggested that some people have different experiences of foods – for example, experiencing fruit and vegetables as bitter in nature (Brigham et al., 2018).
- Concern about the negative effects of food
    - The avoidance of certain food is driven by the fear of negative effects, such as choking, gagging, vomiting, and gastrointestinal distress.
    - This presentation can develop at any age and often has an acute onset, with a shorter duration of illness. It often develops following a traumatic event such as witnessing or experiencing

choking. People may start by avoiding a certain type of food. This then progresses over time, resulting in restriction of a wider range of foods.

> I have never taken any pleasure in eating food. I've never been a "foodie" or used food as comfort.
>
> Sarah Miller

> I struggled with fresh food, because it could be slightly different each time: more bitter, sweeter, and so on.
>
> Sarah Miller

A key factor differentiating ARFID from AN is the lack of body- and shape-related concerns. This can be difficult to differentiate: due to the egosyntonic nature of AN, people living with this may often hide or deny these concerns and thus may be incorrectly diagnosed with ARFID. However, with the weight gain that is often encouraged in ARFID, these concerns (if present) would become more apparent. In addition, people with ARFID are often accepting of the fact they are underweight, and may be keen to correct this.

ARFID is commonly comorbid with other mental health conditions, including anxiety disorders, mood disorders, and OCD (Brigham et al., 2018), and it can in turn act as a risk factor for other eating disorder development (Kennedy et al., 2022).

CONSULTATION WITH A DOCTOR

People with ARFID may present initially to their GP, and this is often due to concern from parents and family about their limited food intake. It is important for the doctor to develop a rapport and build trust with all involved. At times, this may be a challenge, due to the intense feelings of anxiety people feel when being challenged to eat certain foods. It may be helpful for the doctor to include other people (e.g. family and carers) in assessments, in order to gain a collateral history.

The doctor's assessment will consist of two parts: gaining a history and conducting a physical assessment.

HISTORY

"Taking a history" is the process whereby the doctor talks to the patient and gathers information. They will aim to find out what the person's eating patterns are like, what they eat on a day-to-day basis, and the history of their restrictive intake. For example, they need to assess when the ARFID started. Has their food intake been limited since childhood or did an acute event precipitate it? Do they have a fear of certain consequences if they eat certain foods? A food diary may assist in identifying the person's standard food intake.

The doctor may ask about their appetite and interest in food and what stops them eating certain foods. Is it the taste or texture of foods? In some cases, it may be easier to identify the foods that *are* accepted, rather than those avoided. They will also need to identify the impact this is having on the person's life and functioning – are they able to function well at school or in relationships?

> If I were too cold, too hot (or if my clothing were too uncomfortable), it would become extremely difficult for me to consume any food. It was almost as though I had a "threshold" for sensory discomfort, and if I was already at that threshold then I couldn't manage any food.
>
> Sarah Miller

ASSESSMENT

Due to the potential for malnutrition, a careful physical assessment may be needed. Height, weight, and BMI should be calculated, and in children a weight-for-height percentage may need to be worked out, to assess for faltering growth. They may need some investigations (e.g. blood tests) to identify the effects of malnutrition.

The assessment is important, as it identifies any physical complications that may have developed, which may be similar to those seen in AN. For example, people may become dehydrated, feel dizzy and faint, become intolerant of the cold, and get dry skin and brittle nails. Limited food intake may result in electrolyte changes such as hypokalaemia (low potassium). Females may have a delay in starting their periods (primary amenorrhea) or their periods may stop after having previously established cycles (secondary amenorrhea).

Micronutrient deficiency may develop with the potential for serious vitamin deficiencies. This can lead to a range of complications, such as (Brigham et al., 2018):

- Vitamin B12 and folate deficiency can cause anaemia.
- Vitamin C deficiency can result in scurvy.
- Vitamin A deficiency can cause poor night vision and night blindness.
- Vitamin K deficiency can result in easy bruising and bleeding.

Poor oral intake may result in gastrointestinal symptoms such as delayed gastric emptying and constipation (Coglan & Otasowie, 2019), which in turn can cause a lack of appetite, early satiety (feeling full quickly on eating), bloating, and abdominal pain, which may further perpetuate the disorder.

POTENTIAL FOR BLIND SPOTS, MISDIAGNOSES, AND BIASES

When someone is assessed for ARFID, the doctor will often consider alternative "differential" diagnoses – other conditions which may explain the symptoms they are presenting with. Conditions to consider are those that result in poor oral intake and/or weight loss, such as problems with the gastrointestinal system, infections (TB, HIV), systemic disorders (e.g. hypothyroidism, Addison's disease, systemic lupus erythematosus), effects of medication, cancers, and other mental illnesses (e.g. anxiety disorders, mood disorders, AN).

Picky eating (a restriction and limitation of food intake) is a common, often transient, phase of childhood. It is important to differentiate this from ARFID. With picky eating, children will restrict their food intake, but maintain their nutritional status and not require any further nutritional support or supplementation. Their eating doesn't have a detrimental impact on their life and functioning. Over time, picky eating will resolve, whereas ARFID requires intervention to aid recovery.

TREATMENT

There is currently no standardised treatment for ARFID, and research into the efficacy of treatment models is ongoing. However, it is generally accepted that care should be provided by a multidisciplinary team (MDT), ideally including a medical doctor (preferably a gastroenterology specialist), psychiatrist and mental health team, dietitian, occupational therapist, and speech and language (SALT) support.

ARFID can be considered as either short term or long term, and this has an implication for its treatment and outcomes. Short-term ARFID has an acute onset – often a clear trigger, such as witnessing or experiencing choking. People with short-term ARFID will have a history of previously normal eating patterns, so treatment addressing nutrition and anxiety can result in a faster recovery. Long-term ARFID, on the other hand, will present with a long history of restrictive eating, often in the absence of a previously normal eating pattern. It will require long-term intensive treatment (Zimmerman et al., 2017).

> Recovery from ARFID is a long, slow process of gradually being more adventurous with food. I'm learning to lean into my sensory threshold, and to try new foods on the days when I'm much farther away from that "threshold".
>
> Sarah Miller

The primary aim of treatment is to increase food intake and reduce the psychopathology driving restrictive behaviours. Therefore, there are two aspects to the treatment of ARFID: addressing the person's eating behaviours, and restoring their nutritional status.

Behavioural and psychiatric treatments that have been discussed include CBT (given individually or in a family-based setting), intensive behavioural interventions, parent training, and systemic desensitisation.

Medication has been discussed in the treatment of ARFID, including the use of antidepressants (SSRIs – selective serotonin reuptake inhibitors and Mirtazapine), antipsychotics (olanzapine), and Cyproheptadine (used to stimulate appetite), but currently there is insufficient evidence to support the use of these.

NUTRITION

Nutritional support, involving an increase in volume and or variety of foods, should be done with the support of a dietitian. People may need nutritional, vitamin, and mineral supplementation during treatment. If they are medically unstable, it may be safest to do this in an inpatient hospital setting.

Similar to AN, those with ARFID may be at risk of refeeding syndrome, and they may need close medical monitoring via blood tests to identify any electrolyte abnormalities and to initiate prompt treatment.

Some people may need nasogastric (NG) feeding if they are malnourished. This can be highly beneficial in managing their malnutrition, but it doesn't come without any risks. The visceral sensation (such as feeling full or bloated and abdominal pain) which develops as a result of NG feeding may have a worsening and negative impact on the person's perception of food (Katzman et al., 2019), which aggravates their psychopathology and food avoidance. In addition, if the person has a lack of appetite or apathy towards food, giving NG feeding may reduce the person's desire to eat further and they may develop a greater dissociation between hunger cues and eating.

NG feeding should therefore only be used as a temporary measure, and weaning should occur at the earliest opportunity. This may be done through a slow reduction in NG feed, which would stimulate appetite. Close monitoring of this may be necessary, as there is a potential for initial weight loss (Coglan & Otasowie, 2019).

Further information about treatment can be found in Chapter 11.

SUMMARY

- Avoidant restrictive food intake disorder (ARFID) is a relatively newly recognised eating disorder, so the current understanding of the disorder is limited but growing.
- The onset of ARFID is typically in childhood, and is more common in males and those with pre-existing neurodiversity.
- Biological risk factors include genetics and gastrointestinal disorders such as reflux and food allergies.
- Psychological risk factors include pre-existing anxiety disorders and OCD.
- Sociocultural risk factors include parental pressure to eat and limited exposure to certain foods.
- People presenting to a doctor with ARFID will often have a long history of restrictive eating and may have been referred to different medical teams, such as gastroenterology, in the past.
- ARFID describes a heterogenous group of conditions, characterised by a restriction in food intake which is not driven by a desire

to change their body shape or weight, and results in nutritional deficiency, dependence on nutritional supplementation, and/or functional impairment.

- The DSM-5 identifies three different types of presentation of ARFID – a lack of interest in food, avoidance of food based on its sensory characteristics, and concern about the negative effects of food.
- ARFID is commonly comorbid with other mental health conditions, including mood disorders, anxiety disorders, and OCD.
- The initial assessment of ARFID may be carried out by a GP and consists of a history (a discussion with the person to understand their current symptoms, duration of illness, and food intake), followed by an examination to look for any complications which may have developed.
- There is currently no standardised treatment for ARFID, but the primary aim suggested is the increase of food intake and reduction of psychopathology driving the restrictive behaviours.

REFERENCES

American Psychiatric Association. (2013). *Diagnostic and statistical manual of mental disorders: DSM-5*, 5th edition. Washington, DC: American Psychiatric Publishing.

Brigham, K. S., Manzo, L. D., Eddy, K. T., & Thomas, J. J. (2018). Evaluation and treatment of avoidant/restrictive food intake disorder (ARFID) in Adolescents. *Current Pediatrics Reports*, 6(2), 107–113. https://doi.org/10.1007/s40124-018-0162-y.

Coglan, L., & Otasowie, J. (2019). Avoidant/restrictive food intake disorder: what do we know so far?. *BJPsych Advances*, 25(2), 90–98.

Inoue, T., Otani, R., Iguchi, T., Ishii, R., Uchida, S., Okada, A., ... & Sakuta, R. (2021). Prevalence of autism spectrum disorder and autistic traits in children with anorexia nervosa and avoidant/restrictive food intake disorder. *Biopsychosocial Medicine*, 15(1), 9. https://doi.org/10.1186/s13030-021-00212-3.

Katzman, D. K., Norris, M. L., & Zucker, N. (2019). Avoidant restrictive food intake disorder: first do no harm. *International Journal of Eating Disorders*, 52(4), 459–461. https://doi.org/10.1002/eat.23021.

Kennedy, H. L., Dinkler, L., Kennedy, M. A., Bulik, C. M., & Jordan, J. (2022). How genetic analysis may contribute to the understanding of avoidant/restrictive food intake disorder (ARFID). *Journal of Eating Disorders*, 10(1), 53. https://doi.org/10.1186/s40337-022-00578-x.

Pollard, N. J. (2019). The ABCDE tool for spotting the early signs of an eating disorder. *The Family Files*, 4. FamilyMentalWealth.com/FamilyFiles.

Thomas, J. J., Lawson, E. A., Micali, N., Misra, M., Deckersbach, T., & Eddy, K. T. (2017). Avoidant/restrictive food intake disorder: a three-dimensional model of neurobiology with implications for etiology and treatment. *Current Psychiatry Reports*, 19(8), 54. https://doi.org/10.1007/s11920-017-0795-5.

World Health Organization. (2022). *ICD-11: international classification of diseases*, 11th revision. https://icd.who.int/.

Zimmerman, J., & Fisher, M. (2017). Avoidant/restrictive food intake disorder (ARFID). *Current Problems in Pediatric and Adolescent Health Care*, 47(4), 95–103. https://doi.org/10.1016/j.cppeds.2017.02.005.

PICA
Dr Elizabeth McNaught

BACKGROUND

Pica is an eating disorder which is characterised by the eating of non-food-based substances such as ice, soil, plaster, chalk, plastic, and wool, or raw ingredients such as salt and flour. It is named after the Latin name for a magpie, a bird known for its unusual eating habits, consuming both food and non-food substances. Pica has been recognised for a long time, having first been described by Hippocrates in 400 BCE.

Pica can present in all ages, it is most common in the early years of life (but may continue into adulthood), pregnancy, and in lower socioeconomic groups (Rose et al., 2000). Behaviours may occur at any point in the day, and common triggers include a craving for the substance consumed, boredom, curiosity, and internal tension (Treasure et al., 2020). The presentation is classified according to the substance ingested, and commonly observed presentations include (McNaughten et al., 2017; Santos et al., 2016):

- acuphagia – sharp objects
- amylophagia – laundry starch
- coniophagia – dust
- geophagia – earth/clay
- pagophagia – ice
- plumbophagia – lead
- tricophagia – hair, wool, and other fibres.

DOI: 10.4324/9781003342762-9

It is common in pregnancy to crave non-food substances; pica should only be diagnosed if this behaviour is persistent and severe enough to require medical attention.

The underlying cause of the disorder is unknown, but it has been linked to anaemia and micronutrient deficiency (it is unclear if it is the deficiency driving the abnormal eating patterns, or vice versa) (Miao et al., 2015). Other factors discussed in its presentation include a history of parental neglect and deprivation (McNaughten et al., 2017).

DIAGNOSIS

Doctors make a diagnosis of pica based on the DSM-5 (*Diagnostic and Statistical Manual of Mental Disorders*) and/or the ICD-11 (*International Classification of Diseases*) (American Psychiatric Association, 2013; World Health Organization, 2022).

Diagnostic features drawn from these publications are:

- The persistent eating of non-food, non-nutritive, or raw food items (such as large amounts of salt or flour).
- Eating behaviour is inappropriate to the person's developmental level.
    - It is common for children under 2 years to put a variety of objects and substances in their mouth. After the age of 2, children should be able to identify the difference between food and non-food items.
- Eating behaviour is not considered a normal practice within the person's culture and society.
- Eating behaviour is significant enough to warrant medical care. This may be due to its effect on people's ability to function in daily life, or the risk it poses to their physical health.
- If it occurs in the context of another mental disorder (e.g. schizophrenia) or a medical condition (e.g. pregnancy), pica can only be diagnosed if it is significant enough to require medical attention.

Pica is commonly comorbid with autism spectrum disorder (ASD), ASD characteristics, and intellectual disability (Fields et al., 2021). Other common comorbidities include schizophrenia and physical disorders (Treasure et al., 2020), hair-pulling disorder (trichotillomania), skin-picking disorder (excoriation), and avoidant restrictive food intake disorder (ARFID) (American Psychiatric Association, 2013).

CONSULTATION WITH A DOCTOR

The initial consultation may be with a GP or another medical professional. The latter often occurs if complications have developed – for example, they may present with gastrointestinal obstruction, in which case they may be assessed by a surgeon; or present with poisoning, and thus be seen by an acute medical doctor.

HISTORY

"Taking a history" is the process whereby the doctor talks to the patient and gathers information. People living with pica, or their parents and carers, may have clear concerns about their eating habits, which they bring to the doctor. However, children may fear being told off for their eating habits, or they feel embarrassed about it, and others may not recognise it as an issue. Therefore, doctors should ask directly what people are eating, as well as look for other symptoms that may develop due to complications, such as abdominal pain, nausea, or dizziness. Outside of the eating of non-food items, people living with pica may eat a normal balanced diet.

Parents and siblings can be useful sources of information, not only about what they eat on a day-to-day basis but also what they may consume outside of mealtimes – for example, during play time. A food diary may help to identify everything that is consumed in a fixed period of time.

A wider history may be taken to understand the person's developmental history. Have they reached all their developmental milestones growing up? Is there concern about developmental delay? Do they have any symptoms of anaemia or micronutrient deficiencies? Do they have any medical conditions that may predispose to pica.

ASSESSMENT

The doctor may need to conduct a physical assessment, to look for any complications that may develop. Potential complications include poisoning, infection, and obstruction.

Lead is a commonly ingested substance in pica, and this may lead to lead poisoning. This is often asymptomatic or presents with minor symptoms, such as feeling tired, headaches, irritability, abdominal pain, nausea, loss of appetite, and constipation. In severe cases, it may lead to nerve damage or seizures, and can be fatal.

Infections may develop due to ingestion of soil. For example, toxocariasis is an infection caused by the ingestion of small worms found in fox, dog, and cat faeces. Infection may be asymptomatic and resolve quickly. If it spreads, it may present with symptoms such as fevers, fatigue, changes to vision, rashes, and abdominal pain.

Gastrointestinal obstructions may develop if substances – for example, hair – are not broken down in the gastrointestinal system and they form a blockage. This may present with abdominal pain, nausea, and vomiting, and the person may not be able to pass wind or faeces. This is a medical emergency and requires specialist hospital management.

> Teeth may also be damaged due to eating hard and inedible substances. This may lead to damage to the surface of the teeth.

Further investigations may be needed – for example, blood tests to check for anaemia and lead levels, stool samples to look for any infection, and imaging (such as an abdominal X-ray) to look for a blockage.

TREATMENT

There is currently no standardised treatment for pica, and research into the efficacy of treatment models is ongoing. However, it is generally accepted that care should be provided by a multidisciplinary team (MDT), which would normally include a medical doctor, dietitian, dentist, and psychologist.

In children, young people, and those who are pregnant, pica will often spontaneously resolve. However, clinical interventions may be necessary, maybe through simple education around the disorders and its potential risks, or through more intensive treatments, such as behavioural interventions, which may include positive reinforcement (using play or a fun activity as a reward for not engaging in pica behaviours), aversive therapy (linking pica behaviour to a negative experience such as an unpleasant smell or taste), or physical interventions to prevent pica behaviours (such as masks to stop substances being eaten).

If the person living with pica is found to be anaemic or to have micronutrient deficiencies, then treatment of these deficiencies or food supplements may be needed.

Further information about treatment can be found in Chapter 11.

SUMMARY

- Pica is an eating disorder characterised by the eating of non-food-based substances.
- This eating behaviour is not appropriate to the person's developmental level or part of socially or culturally accepted practices.
- The eating patterns seen negatively affect people's ability to function or causes them significant physical harm.
- Pica can present in all ages. It is most common in the early years, pregnancy, and in lower socioeconomic groups.
- The underlying cause is unknown. It has been linked to micronutrient deficiency and anaemia and is commonly comorbid with autism spectrum disorder and intellectual disability.
- Outside of pica behaviours, people often eat a normal balanced diet.
- The initial assessment may be with a GP or other health care professional, and they may present due to their own (or loved ones') concerns around their eating habits or the presence of complications.
- Complications include damage to teeth, poisoning (e.g. lead), infection (e.g. toxocariasis), and gastrointestinal obstruction.
- There is currently no standardised treatment for pica.
- Treatments that have been discussed include behavioural interventions such as positive reinforcement and aversive therapy.
- In children, young people and those who are pregnant, pica will often spontaneously resolve.

REFERENCES

American Psychiatric Association. (2013). *Diagnostic and statistical manual of mental disorders: DSM-5*, 5th edition. Washington, DC: American Psychiatric Publishing.

Fields, V. L., Soke, G. N., Reynolds, A., Tian, L. H., Wiggins, L., Maenner, M. …, & Schieve, L. A. (2021). Pica, autism, and other disabilities. *Pediatrics*, 147(2), e20200462. https://doi.org/10.1542/peds.2020-0462.

McNaughten, B., Bourke, T., & Thompson, A. (2017). Fifteen-minute consultation: the child with pica. *Archives of Disease in Childhood: Education and Practice Edition*, 102(5), 226–229. https://doi.org/10.1136/archdischild-2016-312121.

Miao, D., Young, S. L., & Golden, C. D. (2015). A meta-analysis of pica and micronutrient status. *American Journal of Human Biology*, 27(1), 84–93. https://doi.org/10.1002/ajhb.22598.

Rose, E. A., Porcerelli, J. H., & Neale, A. V. (2000). Pica: common but commonly missed. *Journal of the American Board of Family Practice*, 13(5), 353–358.

Santos, A. M., Benute, G. R., Nomura, R. M., Santos, N. O., De Lucia, M. C., & Francisco, R. P. (2016). Pica and eating attitudes: a study of high-risk pregnancies. *Maternal and Child Health Journal*, 20(3), 577–582. https://doi.org/10.1007/s10995-015-1856-1.

Treasure, J., Duarte, T. A., & Schmidt, U. (2020). Eating disorders. *Lancet*, 395(10227), 899–911. https://doi.org/10.1016/S0140-6736(20)30059-3.

World Health Organization. (2022). *ICD-11: international classification of diseases*, 11th revision. https://icd.who.int/.

RUMINATION DISORDER
Dr Elizabeth McNaught

BACKGROUND

Rumination disorder is an eating disorder characterised by the frequent, recurrent, effortless regurgitation of food, which is then either re-chewed and swallowed or spat out. This regurgitation happens in the absence of any physical cause and without any nausea or retching. People find it a positive and calming experience, and it may ease feelings of unrest and anxiety, thus serving as a self-soothing behaviour.

Rumination disorder was first described in 1618 by Fabricus ab Aquapendende, and the understanding of it has evolved over time. It is currently described as both an eating disorder and a functional gastrointestinal disorder. It has classically been described in children and those with intellectual disability (Bryant-Waugh, 2019), but can develop, and/or present, at any age. Not much is known about the underlying reasons for the disorder, but possible risk factors include historical abuse and neglect (Bryant-Waugh, 2019), lack of stimulation, stressful life events, and difficult relationships with parents (American Psychiatric Association, 2013). Despite it having been described as a disorder for decades, much is unknown about the condition and it remains underrecognised and underdiagnosed.

DIAGNOSIS

Doctors make a diagnosis of rumination disorder based on the DSM-5 (*Diagnostic and Statistical Manual of Mental Disorders*) and/or the ICD-11 (*International Classification of Diseases* (American Psychiatric Association, 2013; World Health Organization, 2022).

DOI: 10.4324/9781003342762-10

Diagnostic features drawn from these publications are:

- The repeated, intentional regurgitation of previously swallowed food.
  - This is either re-chewed and swallowed, or spat out.
- Regurgitation behaviour occurs frequently for at least a month.
- The behaviour occurs in those with a developmental age of at least 2 years old.
  - Before that age, this may be considered normal behaviour.
- Regurgitation is not due to a medical condition or co-existent with anorexia nervosa, bulimia nervosa, binge eating disorder, or avoidant restrictive food intake disorder.
  - If regurgitation behaviour is seen in the context of any of these eating disorders, then it is not diagnosed as a separate disorder and is instead accepted as part of the eating disorder it presents with.
- If it presents in the context of another mental illness or neurodevelopmental condition, then the rumination must be severe enough to need additional care.

Mental health conditions are commonly comorbid, most commonly depression and anxiety (Mousa et al., 2014).

> When Chelsea was an inpatient ... one member of staff noted her difficulties around regurgitation and "re-chewing" as it was recorded.
> Chris Avenell

CONSULTATION WITH A DOCTOR

The initial consultation may be with a GP or another medical professional. People often feel shame and embarrassment about their behaviours and thus may be reluctant to disclose anything, or, if they do, the lack of knowledge and awareness of the disorder may result in it not being diagnosed. Rumination disorder may go undetected for many years.

Even when people do feel able to disclose their symptoms, they are frequently misdiagnosed. Reporting that food returns to the mouth after eating may be interpreted as reflux or vomiting. The person may be given medical treatments such as reflux medication, but this sees little positive physical response.

She was treated for indigestion, heartburn, and nausea and sickness. She was prescribed several drugs over a period of time. These included prochlorperazine (stemetil), baclofen, metoclopramide, cyclizine, and Gaviscon.

Chris Avenell

HISTORY

"Taking a history" is the process whereby the doctor talks to the patient and gathers information. Due to the embarrassment felt, they will need to build a rapport with the patient and gather information over a period of time. It may be necessary to observe mealtimes and to keep food and behaviour logs.

People with rumination disorder may report that regurgitation behaviour happens rapidly after eating (often within minutes, but it can occur up to two hours after food), and after most meals. The food which is brought up will often resemble the food just eaten, both in appearance and taste, and will not be bitter or acidic in nature. In fact, when it does become bitter/acidic, typically regurgitation will cease. To hide the regurgitation, people may be seen to put their hand or tissues to their mouth at the dinner table.

The early symptoms and signs, as far as I was aware, were regurgitation of food after eating and sickness ... I thought this was something that was being done deliberately, to prevent the consumption or absorption of the food that had been eaten.

Chris Avenell

Regurgitation will occur with ease and is a learned behaviour under voluntary control. However, people may deny or struggle to accept this is the case. Regurgitation behaviours may increase during periods of stress (Bryant-Waugh, 2019).

Rumination disorder can have a negative effect on people's functioning. This may be through recognising that this behaviour is socially inappropriate and they feel embarrassed about it, and therefore they may become socially isolated, or they may limit their food intake when with others, to prevent regurgitation behaviours. In children and young people, they may miss significant amounts of school and education; in adults, this may lead to difficulties in relationships and employment.

> Chelsea quickly became very self-conscious about eating with any-one, as she knew that the rumination sounded awful and made her feel awful. She stopped eating around people, even close family. She will attend some social, family events, but won't eat. So, if the family go for a meal, she sits and just has a drink or maybe a couple of mouthfuls of food from my plate. She is worried about eating too much, triggering the rumination and having to go to the toilets. As she won't eat a meal at home with us either, this has led to her being further isolated from wider family and friends.
>
> Chris Avenell

It is important to distinguish the difference between vomiting and regurgitation. Vomiting will often be preceded by nausea, be unintentional, and involve bring up large volumes, all of which are unpleasant in nature.

> I found (and still find) it difficult to deal with. The noise of the regurgitation is awful and sounds as if she is trying to stop herself fully swallowing the food by repeatedly bringing it back up into her mouth. I often wanted to shout at her to stop doing it, although I never did.
>
> Chris Avenell

ASSESSMENT

If rumination disorder is misdiagnosed (as reflux, vomiting, or a gastrointestinal obstruction, for example), then the person may have multiple assessments and investigations, undertaken by different health care professionals. These investigations include endoscopies (medical tests that use a long, thin tube with a small camera to look at the oesophagus and stomach) and scans to look for any blockage or other cause of the symptoms.

Investigations may be required, to exclude medical conditions. However, they are not needed to make a positive diagnosis of rumination disorder, which can be achieved on history alone.

If people struggle to accept that the behaviour is under voluntary control, encouraging them to place a hand on their abdomen should draw their attention to the contraction of the abdominal wall muscles that drives the regurgitation (Fox et al., 2006). If that fails, then another suggested option is manometry (measuring the pressure changes in the gastrointestinal system).

A doctor may need to conduct a physical assessment, to search for any potential complications. For example, blood tests may be carried out to look for any changes to potassium levels. These complications include:

- weight loss
- malnutrition
- growth failure in children
- dental erosion and decay
- halitosis (bad breath)
- damage to the oesophagus
- changes to the levels of electrolytes in the blood
- constipation
- choking.

TREATMENT

There is currently no standardised treatment for rumination disorder, and research into the efficacy of treatment models is ongoing. However, it is generally accepted that a multidisciplinary team (MDT) – including a medical doctor, dietitian, dentist, and psychologist – should provide the care.

One suggested treatment is diaphragmatic breathing, which helps the person to establish control over regurgitation. They should have one hand on their chest, the other on their abdomen, and they should take deep breaths, using their abdomen and allowing for the relaxation of their abdominal wall muscles. During inspiration their abdomen should become distended, and on expiration it should return to normal. The person with rumination disorder should engage in this a set number of times after eating; over time this will help to prevent regurgitation.

Also discussed is cognitive behavioural therapy (CBT) specific to rumination disorder (CBT-RD). Here, the underlying psychopathology driving the behaviour is addressed.

Nutritional support should be provided if there is evidence of malnutrition, and any complications that may develop should be treated accordingly.

Further information about treatment can be found in Chapter 11.

SUMMARY

- Rumination disorder is recognised as both an eating disorder and a functional gastrointestinal disorder.
- It is characterised by the frequent, recurrent, effortless regurgitation of food, which is then either re-chewed and swallowed, or spat out.
- It has classically been described in children and those with intellectual disability, but can develop, and/or present, at any age.
- To be diagnosed as rumination disorder, the behaviour seen must not be due to a medical condition, due to a developmental age of less than 2 years old, or be seen in the context of anorexia nervosa, bulimia nervosa, binge eating disorder, or ARFID.
- Regurgitation typically occurs within minutes of eating, and the food brought up looks and tastes similar to how it was originally ingested.
- People may feel anxious and stressed, and engaging in this behaviour is soothing in nature.
- People may feel shame and embracement around this behaviour and thus limit eating in public or avoid public events where they may need to eat. This may lead to malnutrition and/or social isolation.
- Rumination disorder may be misdiagnosed as reflux or vomiting, and people may have multiple investigations and be started on treatments (e.g. reflux treatment) that don't have any effect.
- Rumination disorder may go for many years without being undetected.
- Potential complications include weight loss, dental decay, halitosis, and changes to the electrolyte levels in the blood.
- One suggested treatment is diaphragmatic breathing, where the person develops a breathing technique that prevents regurgitation.

REFERENCES

American Psychiatric Association. (2013). *Diagnostic and statistical manual of mental disorders: DSM-5*, 5th edition. Washington, DC: American Psychiatric Publishing.

Bryant-Waugh R. (2019). Feeding and eating disorders in children. *Psychiatric Clinics of North America*, 42(1), 157–167. https://doi.org/10.1016/j.psc.2018.10.005.

Fox, M., Young, A., Anggiansah, R., Anggiansah, A., & Sanderson, J. (2006). A 22 year old man with persistent regurgitation and vomiting: case outcome. *British Medical Journal*, 333(7559), 133–137. https://doi.org/10.1136/bmj.333.7559.133.

Mousa, H. M., Montgomery, M., & Alioto, A. (2014). Adolescent rumination syndrome. *Current Gastroenterology Reports*, 16(8), 398. https://doi.org/10.1007/s11894-014-0398-9.

World Health Organization. (2022). *ICD-11: international classification of diseases*, 11th revision. https://icd.who.int/.

11

TREATMENT
Jess Griffiths

INTRODUCTION

There are a range of treatments available for eating disorders which are mostly delivered by a specialist eating disorder multidisciplinary team (MDT). Treatment intensity can vary depending on the level of support that is needed by the patient. Once a patient is referred to a specialist eating disorder service, they are assessed by a member of the team. The team will formulate a diagnosis and offer an evidence-based treatment to the patient.

THE MULTIDISCIPLINARY TEAM (MDT)

There are often many different health care professionals involved in treating a person with an eating disorder. Psychiatrists and medical doctors will often manage risk, prescribe medication, and coordinate care in day and inpatient settings.

Nurses may work as care coordinators (CCOs) or therapists, organising patient's treatment.

Support workers provide a vital role in working alongside families/individuals, with meal support and other areas of care.

Dieticians are key members of the MDT, constructing meal plans and advising nurses and therapists.

Occupational therapists can often work as CCOs and support patients towards rehabilitation back into the community after intensive treatment (National Centre for Collaboration in Mental Health, 2019).

DOI: 10.4324/9781003342762-11

NICE GUIDELINES

Evidence-based treatments for eating disorders are outlined in the National Institute for Health and Care Excellence (NICE, 2017) guidelines. These guidelines are funded by NHS England to evaluate evidence for treatments for common conditions.

The committee that reviews the treatments includes professional experts, service users and carers, and data experts. The committee then reaches a consensus on the best treatments.

REFERRING TO SPECIALIST EATING DISORDER SERVICES (SEDs)

NICE defines the referral process carefully and suggests the following:

- Do not use body mass index (BMI) as a sole measure or duration of illness to determine whether to offer treatment for an eating disorder.
- If an eating disorder is suspected, refer immediately to a community-based, age-appropriate eating disorder service for further assessment or treatment.

Treatment cannot start until the specialist eating disorder service has received information about the weight, height, and physical health status of the individual. It is important to start this process during referral, as it supports the SEDs team to make a quick, comprehensive clinical judgment, and start treatment as soon as possible.

Early intervention is so important in the treatment of eating disorders. Referring quickly can save lives.

TREATMENT SETTINGS

Eating disorders treatment can often be provided on an outpatient basis. Outpatient treatment is treatment within a setting where you are not required to stay overnight in hospital. The outpatient clinic might be situated within a hospital, medical centre, or community treatment centre.

The following outpatient treatments (as outlined in NICE, 2017) have been found to be effective for people with eating disorders. There is also some evidence that these psychological treatments are effective in more intensive care settings.

> If someone was starting this journey, I would say get educated. Eating disorder services say "You know your child", "Treatment at home is the best option", "Your child will recover best with your support", but what that looks like is an underprepared, underqualified, desperate, terrified parent left holding the bomb.
>
> Rochelle Rouse

Outpatient psychological treatments

Psychological therapies are proven to have the greatest impact on reducing eating disorders symptoms. Several outpatient treatments have been identified as effective "first-line" treatments for eating disorders. Psychological therapy is often delivered as part of an MDT care approach. Medical and dietetic input may be needed, and the person's family, carers, and friends are regularly involved in the treatment.

ENHANCED COGNITIVE BEHAVIOURAL THERAPY (CBT-E)

CBT-E (Fairburn, 2008) is a manualised psychological treatment that is "transdiagnostic". This means that the therapy is adaptable in anorexia nervosa (AN), bulimia nervosa (BN), binge eating disorder (BED), and otherwise specified feeding and eating disorders (OSFED). CBT-E primarily focuses on addressing the thoughts, behaviours, and attitudes around food, weight, and shape that maintain the eating disorder.

There are four stages within CBT-E:

1. *Engagement and stabilisation*

   The therapist will seek to engage the patient in the early stages and start to collaboratively understand their eating issues. The main objectives of this stage are to modify and stabilise the person's eating. The therapist asks the patient to keep a record of all food intake, thoughts, feelings, and eating disorder behaviours. This is called "self-monitoring". The therapist will encourage the patient to become an "expert" on themselves and to take ownership of the work to be completed in between sessions. There is an emphasis on personalised education and addressing concerns around weight in this phase. Sessions are often twice weekly within stage 1.

2. *Taking stock*

   In the second phase of CBT-E, progress and motivation of the patient is reviewed. If the patient has successfully implemented regular eating and reduced eating disorder behaviours, a plan is made for the stage 3 sessions.

3. *Body image, dietary restraint and events, mood and eating*

   Stage 3 involves weekly sessions addressing the maintaining factors of the eating disorder. Often this involves addressing concerns about body image and eating, problem solving day-to-day events and mood, and challenging the extreme dietary restraint. Within the end of this stage, discussions around the cessation of sessions and making plans for the future should be addressed.

4. *Ending well*

   Stage 4 focuses on the future and what the patient wants to achieve after they finish therapy. There are decisions around managing setbacks/relapses and how to manage the changes they've already made.

> I was given one-to-one therapy and we explored triggers for my eating behaviour, including events in my past, and ways of tolerating strong emotions. I was also introduced to acceptance and commitment therapy and mindfulness, which I still use today to support my wellbeing.
>
> Sharon Miklosova

Therapist stance

The therapist should be appropriately trained in CBT-E. The therapist takes an individualised approach to CBT-E and creates a formulation flowchart for each patient. This shows the patient how the overevaluation of food, weight, and shape, together with restricted eating and events/moods, can maintain the eating disorder. CBT-E therapists should work alongside the patient in a collaborative, motivational way. There is some evidence to suggest that early behaviour changes in CBT-E lead to more successful outcomes (Turner et al., 2015).

Number of sessions

Patients who have a diagnosis of AN are offered 40 sessions of CBT-E. Longer sessions are offered due to the inclusion of weight restoration within the therapy. Patients with BN or BED are offered 16–20 sessions.

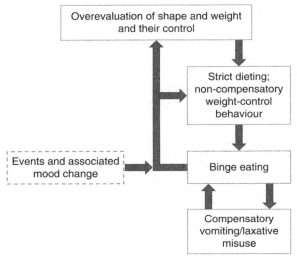

Figure 11.1 An example of a formulation flowchart.

BRIEF COGNITIVE BEHAVIOURAL THERAPY FOR NON-UNDERWEIGHT PATIENTS (CBT-T)

For non–underweight patients, they may be offered an abbreviated version of CBT-E called CBT-T (Waller et al., 2019). It is ten sessions in duration and covers the same topics included in CBT-E.

> The greatest lesson for me is how essential honesty is. You cannot get better by yourself, and, the more you hide and lie, the more space you give to the eating disorder. Every time I am open, and challenge the shame and stigma, I give the eating disorder a little less power.
>
> Marina

> I began to realise that the values and goals of the eating disorder did not align with my personal values. I started to understand that, to have improved quality of life and accomplish any of my future aspirations, I needed to make a change.
>
> Kirsty Stapledon

GROUP COGNITIVE BEHAVIOURAL THERAPY FOR EATING DISORDERS (CBT-ED)

Group CBT-ED is mainly offered for BED and BN. It consists of weekly sessions covering a range of topics, including:

- psychoeducation about starvation
- dietary restraint
- regular eating
- challenging negative thinking around body image.
- relapse prevention and managing triggers.

Patients are asked to keep a self-monitoring diary of eating disorder behaviours, thoughts, emotions, and triggers.

> It's no exaggeration when I say that my 12-week group therapy was a lifesaver. Not only did I learn life tools and skills that helped me to feel more confident about managing my life and my emotions, but being in a group with other people who completely understood and were living this eating disorder too was comforting. The shame began to reduce and I didn't feel as alone as I had before.
>
> Anny Johnson

GUIDED SELF-HELP (GSH)

GSH is a CBT-based low-intensity treatment that is often used alongside a book or a manual. Patients who are appropriate for this treatment often present with mild to moderate symptoms of BN, BED, or disordered eating. The patient is guided through the programme materials (book or manual) by a health professional. GSH supports the person to change their behaviours and unhelpful thinking patterns that might be maintaining the eating disorder.

The intended outcome is for patients to be supported to move to a place where they are able to eat regularly and reduce any eating disorder behaviours.

Sessions

The self-help programme should be supplemented with brief supportive sessions with a practitioner.

Practitioner stance

Practitioners offering GSH do not need to be clinically trained, but they do need to be trained in delivering guided self-help. Their remit is to support the patient to focus exclusively on helping the person follow the programme and adhere to the GSH materials.

NICE guidance

If GSH for BN or BED is not effective, contraindicated, or unacceptable, after four weeks of treatment, then group CBT-ED should be offered (see above).

MAUDSLEY MODEL OF ANOREXIA NERVOSA TREATMENT FOR ADULTS

The Maudsley model of anorexia nervosa treatment for adults (MANTRA) (Schmidt et al., 2019) is a cognitive–interpersonal therapy which has demonstrated effectiveness as an outpatient psychological treatment for adults with AN.

MANTRA aims to address the biological, social, emotional, and cognitive factors which maintain AN by identifying what keeps people stuck in the cycle of AN. A unique formulation of the "vicious flower of AN" seeks to identify:

- The personality traits and supports the person brings to AN (the flowerpot).
- The factors that might keep the AN going. These factors are the individual petals on the "vicious flower of AN". The petals might represent thinking styles (detail focus), the valued nature of AN, emotional processing, life experiences, and relationships with others.
- The mismatch between the resources/supports and the AN petals.

The therapist works alongside the patient to create this unique formulation and they work together to understand the negative cycles that are created through negative thinking or through using AN to numb feelings.

The purpose of therapy is to work through each factor/petal, using a module in the book to create a "virtuous flower of recovery". Not every chapter needs to be covered, and the therapist works alongside the patient to identify the relevant material.

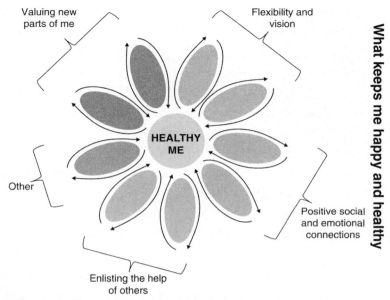

Figure 11.2 Virtuous flower of health and happiness.

MANTRA seeks to support people with AN to develop better ways of coping and overcoming challenges. This is achieved by knowing their personality and supports better, and using positive and non-maladaptive ways to cope.

Sessions

Patients are typically offered 20–30 sessions and the therapist works alongside the patient to determine how many sessions are required.

Therapist stance

Therapists take a motivational stance and use the therapeutic relationship to allow the patient to feel "seen, heard, and understood". It is important that the therapist encourages the patient to move towards their "non-anorexic" identity and that they emphasise that the person has the resources they need to change their behaviour and to recover. Therapists should have completed the appropriate MANTRA training to deliver this therapy.

> The most challenging part of my journey was transitioning from an anorexic mind to a recovered mind. It was stepping back into the world again, being met with daily life stressors, challenges, and feeling intensely the feeling which I'd used anorexia to numb out. The transition to being myself again. I believe this is where the real recovery happens. It's when I'm faced with challenges and uncomfortable feelings, and I choose a response that is kind, compassionate, and wise.
>
> Florence Greenwood

SPECIALIST SUPPORTIVE CLINICAL MANAGEMENT

Specialist supportive clinical management (SSCM) (McIntosh et al., 2006) is offered to patients with AN and consists of several therapeutic components:

- Clinical management which prioritises the establishment of normal eating and weight restoration.
- Targeted psycho-education and advice about eating disorders.
- Therapy to address weight/shape concerns.
- Supportive psychotherapy, to allow the person and their therapist to respond to other life issues that are important for the person, including those that might impact on the eating disorder.

SSCM moves through three different phases, focusing on:

1. Identifying symptoms, agreeing a goal weight and providing a personalised formulation supported by psychoeducation.
2. Nutritional education, which focuses on the person's physical state alongside supportive therapy.
3. Finishing treatment, setting goals for the future and planning to maintain goals.

SSCM seeks to support people to help them establish a link between their symptoms and their eating behaviour and weight, and then to support them to return gradually to normal eating and weight restoration.

Sessions

SSCM is delivered over 20–30 once-weekly individual therapy sessions (depending on severity of symptoms). The last four sessions are often scheduled one month apart.

Therapist stance

SSCM should be delivered by an eating-disorders-trained clinician with a high degree of experience and training. The aim is to build on the existing core skills and strengths of the eating disorder clinicians so they can offer clinical management and supportive psychotherapy. SSCM therapists should offer a flexible approach to sessions where patients can create their own agenda and talk through issues they are already aware of. Often, patients are offered SSCM when they have tried other therapeutic approaches.

> Mental fitness is more than the absence of mental illness. I see recovery as something you have to work at and maintain. And being mentally fit is about investing in yourself, building up your resilience, and coping tools throughout life's natural challenges. I don't see relapse as fatal any more, and try and focus my energy on getting back on track. I now see that berating myself for my struggles was completely unproductive and find solace in knowing that, whilst I may not be able to control all my circumstances, I can control how I react to them. Every time I can challenge the eating disorder voice, which still rears its ugly head in times of high stress, it becomes a little quieter and my hope for a life eating-disorder-free becomes a little greater.
>
> Kirsty Stapledon

FOCAL DYNAMIC THERAPY (FDT)

FDT is a psychodynamic-oriented individual therapy offered to patients with AN. It mainly focuses on unconscious symptomatic, unhealthy relationship patterns, central life-threatening themes, and challenges relating to the structure or aspects of the person's personality. FDT aims to support people to reduce eating disorder symptoms through addressing eating-disorder-related beliefs, self-esteem issues, and depression, as well as working with the family.

Therapy is divided into three phases:

1. Establishing the therapeutic relationship, addressing AN behaviours and beliefs and building self-esteem.
2. Reflecting on how they manage their relationships and how these relationships might impact the AN.
3. Ending therapy – learning to use the skills they've learned in FDT in daily life.

Sessions

It is not unusual for 40–50 sessions of FDT to be offered to patients.

Therapist stance

FDT therapists have an empathic and accepting stance. They validate the person's thoughts and feelings while encouraging them to express "unacceptable or uncomfortable emotions". Therapists seek to explore unconscious, preconscious impulses and anxieties. The therapy also draws on knowledge around the ways that transference and countertransference operate and are addressed within psychodynamic therapy.

> Letting go of my eating disorder was also difficult at first. My eating disorder was my way of coping, and letting it go meant facing my feelings, even the uncomfortable ones. This also meant I had to find "me" away from my eating disorder. This didn't mean forgetting my eating disorder ever happened; it just meant making sure I embraced all parts of me – my values, my loves, my loved ones – and all parts of my life.
>
> Jess Sharman

CHILDREN AND YOUNG PEOPLE OUTPATIENT THERAPY

Family therapy for anorexia nervosa (FT-AN)

FT-AN can be delivered to one family or to multiple families (multi-family therapy, or MFT; Lock & Le Grange, 2012). The aim of this therapy is to equip the parents to refeed their child, to restore their weight to a healthy level (appropriate for their age). Once weight restoration has been achieved, FT-AN should seek to

Table 11.1 Treatment summary for adult outpatient psychological therapy

Adults	CBT-E (groups)	CBT (individual)	MANTRA	SSCM	GSH	FPT
Anorexia nervosa	No	Yes	Yes	Yes	No	Offered if CBT, MANTRA, or SSCM not effective
Bulimia nervosa	No	Offered if GSH for BN not effective	No	No	Yes	No
Binge eating disorder	Yes	Offered if group CBT-E not effective	No	No	Yes	No
OSFED★	If appropriate	If appropriate	If appropriate	If appropriate	If appropriate	If appropriate

Source: NICE (2017).

Note: ★Because OSFED isn't a clearly defined diagnostic category, patients should be offered treatment and therapies according to the eating disorder the OFSED presentation most closely represents (e.g. AN).

address issues around identity and hand back control of eating to the young person.

Young people should be given the opportunity to have single family sessions (if they are allocated to MFT) and individual sessions away from their family unit if they request it. Siblings are often included in the sessions too.

Family therapy for AN (FT-AN) has three phases:

1. The therapist engages with the family and motivates the parents to make changes to the young person's eating. Parents are charged to "take back control" of all food/mealtimes, and a meal plan is given as soon as a diagnosis is confirmed (this could be at the end of assessment). There is a biological emphasis – that AN involves starvation, and food will aid recovery. Families are given the skills to refeed their child and the therapy discusses eating disorder behaviours, to ensure the young person achieves weight restoration. During therapeutic sessions, the young person is weighed, and the focus of the session is determined by the change in weight (loss, maintenance, or restoration).

2. The aim of this phase is to start handing back control to the young person, while navigating any lapses. Family issues and relationships are simultaneously addressed, and the focus slowly moves away from weight and food. The structure of these sessions can vary, but it is ideal to allow time with the parents on their own, time with the young person on their own, and time together (Lock & Le Grange, 2012).

3. The last phase involves addressing adolescent issues and the end of treatment. To reach phase 3, the young person should be weight-restored and in control of their eating behaviours. This phase focuses on addressing normal adolescent issues and strengthening a sense of identity without the eating disorder.

Sessions

Families are offered 18–20 sessions over a 12-month period. Treatment time can vary depending on progress and progression through the stages. The sessions should be reviewed four weeks after the commencement of therapy, and then at regular intervals, to establish the duration of treatment and how often the sessions should be.

Therapist stance

Therapists delivering FT-AN should be appropriately trained in the model, as well as informed eating disorder clinicians. Initially, therapists are encouraged to show "grave concern" at the outset of treatment, to encourage families to feel empowered to take charge of weight restoration and to coach their child through to recovery from the AN. There should never be any blame apportioned to family members of carers, and it is important to support them as our "best resource" for eating disorder recovery.

1. Remember you will never win an argument with anorexia.
2. Think very carefully what to say before you say anything at all.
3. Use patience by the bucket-load.
4. Take control over the diet from day one – be strict, don't accept excuses, and change whatever mealtime plan you had made.
5. It's OK to be suspicious. Check those pockets, watch and support after a meal, don't believe what you are told. Be firm but fair.
6. Set out plans and boundaries together.

Nicky Smith

FAMILY THERAPY FOR BULIMIA NERVOSA (FT-BN)

FT-BN is similar to the therapy used for AN. However, there is more of an emphasis placed on disrupting compensatory behaviours such as vomiting, laxatives, and exercise. In phase 1, the parents are encouraging to establish regular eating and take control of any compensatory methods. In phases 2 and 3, independence is encouraged, and control around food is handed back to the young person.

Sessions

FT-BN typically involves 18–20 sessions over a six-month period.

COGNITIVE BEHAVIOURAL THERAPY FOR EATING DISORDERS (CBT-ED)

Individual CBT-ED may be offered to the young person. CBT-ED for young people is very similar to the CBT-ED treatment for adults (see above). While adolescents will receive CBT-ED on their own, there will also be sessions offered to parent/carers.

Sessions

- CBT-ED for AN: 40 sessions may be offered, with frequent sessions during the beginning of treatment. Additional sessions should be offered to include parents/carers.
- CBT-ED for BN: 18 sessions may be offered, with additional sessions offered to include parents/carers.

ADOLESCENT-FOCUSED PSYCHOTHERAPY FOR ANOREXIA NERVOSA (AFP-AN)

The principles of AFP-AN involve empowering the young person to relinquish control of the eating disorder, in order to regain their normal adolescent life, values, goals, and healthy development.

AFP-AN suggests that AN is an unhealthy coping mechanism for one of the following reasons:

- It is a way of controlling and/or covertly expressing feelings of anger, and/or as a method of controlling others in the family system.
- It is a way of compensating for feelings of depression and/or low self-esteem, in which compulsive behaviours like restriction and weight loss serve as a substitute achievement, distracting from underlying feelings of failure.
- It is an alternative identity or personality – an anchoring point around which to organise a sense of self for someone whose identity is otherwise impoverished or fragmented.
- It is a way to delay growing up, often prolonging a dependent relationship with parents/carers.

AFT-AN follows three phases:

- *Phase 1*: establish therapeutic relationship, assess motivation, develop a case formulation, actively encourage weight restoration.
- *Phase 2*: encourage separation and individuation: encourage exploration of individuation issues of adolescence (self-efficacy, school and work goals, social identity) with an emphasis on establishing developmentally appropriate independence from the family; increase the ability to tolerate negative emotions.
- *Phase 3*: coping strategies for adolescent problems and encouraging behaviours or strategies that will lead to independence.

Sessions

Sessions typically consist of 32–40 individual sessions over 12–18 months, with more regular sessions early on (to help the person build a relationship with the practitioner and motivate them to change their behaviour). Additional sessions with parents/carers may be offered if appropriate.

Therapist stance

The therapeutic relationship itself is a crucial component of AFP, with the therapist taking both a nurturing and directive stance to help guide, shape, model, and practise behaviour changes throughout treatment.

Table 11.2 Treatment summary for children and young people outpatient psychological therapy

	FT-AN or MFT-AN	FT-BN	AFP-AN	CBT-ED
Anorexia nervosa	Yes	No	Offered if FT-AN not effective	Offered if FT-AN not effective
Bulimia nervosa	No	Yes	No	Offered if FT-BN not effective
*OSFED**	If appropriate	If appropriate	If appropriate	If appropriate

Source: NICE (2017).

Note: *Because OFSED isn't a clearly defined diagnostic category, patients should be offered treatment and therapies according to the eating disorder the OFSED presentation most closely represents (e.g. AN).

For children and young people with BED, they should be offered the same treatments that are recommended for adults (see Table 11.2).

INPATIENT AND DAY PATIENT TREATMENT

Sometimes people with eating disorders need more intensive treatment than can be offered in the community. We know that the best place for people to manage their recovery is in a community setting. However, if the physical risk of the person becomes too difficult to manage in the community, an age-appropriate inpatient or day patient programme should be offered to enable medical stabilisation and to initiate refeeding. Inpatient admissions should never be offered solely for psychological recovery (NICE, 2017). This decision to admit to day patient or inpatient care should not be based on BMI but on the need of actively monitored risks such as blood tests, electrocardiograms (ECGs), and physical observations. The person's support network also needs to be considered within this decision.

Within a day on the inpatient treatment programme, the patients are supported to eat a weight restoration meal plan. They attend support groups after they have eaten and can attend therapeutic groups to understand their eating disorder recovery in a more comprehensive way. The length of stay in this setting will vary according to the progress made. It is important that a lot of support is given on discharge from the inpatient service, to ensure that the person can maintain their recovery back in the community.

I wanted to get better, I wanted to get back to my life and get rid of the cruel eating disorder voice that plagued my every waking thought, but, like most people with anorexia, I did not want to gain weight. I was adamant that it wasn't necessary to recover, despite everything my treatment team were telling me.

At that point in my illness, I couldn't fathom how I would ever cope with gaining weight and existing in a healthy body. I couldn't imagine how I would be able to bear it, and when I did first dip my toe into the weight restoration process, it was almost unbearable. I felt extraordinarily uncomfortable in my own skin, like I wanted to climb out of myself and be anywhere but in my body. When the scales crept up, I screamed and cried while my eating disorder said the cruellest things.

In hindsight, I wish I'd got the whole thing over and done with much sooner. Weight restoration is one small part of recovery, but it makes everything else so much easier. You can't do much while your body and brain are in starvation and thinking of nothing but food. I could barely hold a conversation, let alone engage in therapy. It was only once I was a healthier weight, and eating regularly, that the psychological work started to make sense. I began to understand the underlying reasons for my eating disorder and the things that were keeping it alive, which in turn meant I could make the changes needed to start building my life back up.

Laura Hanton

Intensive home treatment

Some specialist eating disorder services have started to provide intensive home treatment for patients. This involves health professionals conducting meal support and therapy in the home.

Managing physical risk in treatment

There can be serious physical complications to having an eating disorder, and patients need to be carefully medically monitored. Table 11.3 is adapted from the Royal College of Psychiatrists (2022) *Managing Medical Emergencies in Eating Disorders* (MEED) guidelines, and gives an example of how risk is assessed in eating disorders in the categories of BMI, heart rate, and rate of weight loss. These are not the only factors to consider when assessing medical risk in patients experiencing eating disorders. The MEED guidelines (Royal College of Psychiatrists, 2022) outline all the physical health checks that should be completed when assessing and treating eating disorders.

Table 11.3 All-age risk assessment

	BMI	Heart rate (awake)	Rate of weight loss
Green (low impending risk to life)	Under 18: m% BMI >80% Over 18: BMI >15	>50	Recent weight loss of <500g/ week or fluctuating weight
Amber (alert to high concern for impending risk to life)	Under 18: m% BMI 70–80% Over 18: BMI 13–14.9	40–50	Recent loss of weight of 500–999g/week for two consecutive weeks in an undernourished patient
Red (high impending risk to life)	Under 18 years: m% BMI 35 <70% Over 18: BMI <13	<40	Recent loss of weight of ≥1 kg/week for two weeks (consecutive) in an undernourished patient Rapid weight loss at any weight, e.g. in obesity or ARFID

Royal College of Psychiatrists (2022).

I had weekly physical monitoring at my local GP surgery with a nurse, who I got on with really well. She always made extra time for us to have a chat, which I found to be one of the most helpful things in my treatment – just being listened to, her genuine encouragement. I remember one time she asked me to bring in pictures from a dance performance I was in. This was really special, because I'd had to stop dance due to my physical health (consequential from the eating disorder), and I'd just recently been allowed to go back to it. The fact she cared enough to see the pictures was so meaningful and encouraging to me.

Jess Sharman

Dietetic input and refeeding

Dietitians are almost always involved in the treatment for an eating disorder. If a patient is assessed as underweight, they will be supported to implement a refeeding plan; if the patient is a child or adolescent, the family will be supported to implement refeeding. The dietitian will assess the required energy intake of the patient and then make a meal plan to increase their intake, usually based around the structure of three meals and three snacks. Sometimes, fortified "build-up" drinks are included in this plan, although this is usually avoided to ensure that patients maintain their intake of solid foods. The dietitian will regularly review this meal plan to ensure that the patient is making good progress with their weight restoration. It is expected that patients in the community will gain around 0.5 kg per week; patients in an inpatient setting, 1 kg per week.

When a person with an eating disorder is struggling to increase their energy intake, finds it too difficult to consume meals and snacks, and their physical health is compromised because of this, they may be offered a liquid replacement through a nasogastric tube (NGT).

If a patient is around normal weight, they may still see the dietitian to review how they can eat more regularly so they are not physically hungry. Again, they are often prescribed a meal plan of three meals and three snacks. Being physically hungry can lead to bingeing, which can cause the patient to feel out of control of their eating.

Once a patient has implemented regular eating, any emotional or psychological triggers can be identified and explored.

Location of treatment for patients with compromised physical health requiring NGT

When clinicians assess that a patient has reached a point in their treatment where the physical risk is too high for them to be managed in the community, they may be treated in a specialist eating disorder psychiatric unit or in an acute medical setting. NGT feeding may be required, because the patient finds it too distressing or difficult to manage solid foods. Clinicians have very difficult decisions to make, weighing up the physical risk of the patient and their rehabilitation towards normal eating and recovery.

Compulsory treatment

Sometimes in the treatment process, health professionals have to consider whether lifesaving treatment should be given to patients without their consent. This would only be administered under a clear legal framework, such as the Mental Health Act (MHA, 1983) or Mental Capacity Act (2005) (Royal College of Psychiatrists, 2022). There are also contexts (such as in emergency departments) where health professionals will use "holding powers" to keep patients from leaving the hospital if the risk they present to themselves or others is too high.

The treatment offered in this situation may involve NGT feeding under restraint. Ethical decisions around this type of treatment are incredibly difficult for health professionals, but the general consensus from eating disorder specialists is that this type of treatment is a "last resort" and every effort should be made to engage the patient in a therapeutic relationship.

CONFIDENTIALITY IN TREATMENT

Adults

The therapeutic relationship and trust are central to the effective management and treatment of eating disorders. Adult patients have an expectation that their treatment will remain confidential and that personal details surrounding their treatment will only be shared within the MDT. While confidentiality should be upheld, it is important that carers should be offered support from health care professionals, whether or not their loved one has consented to information sharing (Treasure et al., 2016) (see Chapter 12).

Children and young people

All children under the age of 16 should be assessed through Gillick competency to ascertain whether they have capacity to make informed decisions around their care (McNaught et al., 2022). If they are deemed to have capacity to make decisions around their care, they can withhold consent to information about their treatment (including their carers) being shared. Children over the age of 16 are presumed to have capacity and therefore can consent (or not) to such information being shared.

Confidentiality and capacity

Patients receiving treatment have the right to refuse consent to information sharing, even if they lack capacity. Health professionals consider the best interests of the patient and are generally positive about carers and friends being involved in treatment (unless there is a clear reason why they shouldn't be, e.g. there is a safeguarding issue).

OSFED

As discussed in Chapter 7, people with OSFED are offered the treatment that their eating disorder most clearly resembles.

> The denial process lasted a long time. Being in and out of services, but no one could help, because I didn't want to be helped. But things changed when I slowly realised that this is not who I want to be. I didn't want to be the girl who hated herself and hated life. I used to be the girl that was a breath of fresh air and who brought joy into people's lives, and then I turned into what I used to call myself, a tragedy. It was actually my auntie who brought this new sense of hope and motivation out of me, and to be honest I wasn't entirely sure how. I wasn't sure whether it was her unconditional love for me and the ability to see my spark when I couldn't, or her patience and lack of judgment, that provided me with a safe space to be completely honest and vulnerable, which in turn allowed me to grow into this new version of me away from my eating disorder.
>
> Anjali Heer

Atypical anorexia treatment (AAT)

Treatment for AAT is very similar to those who are experiencing AN. Often, those with a higher BMI have thoughts and behaviours that are very similar to AN. Patients are often expected to weight-restore (if needed) and attend psychological therapy.

Bulimia nervosa and binge eating disorder (of low frequency/and or limited duration)

Patients with these eating disorders often experience similar thoughts and behaviours to those experiencing BN and BED. The main difference is that their behaviours are below the threshold expected in order to be diagnosed with those conditions. They should be offered GSH–BN, GSH–BED, group CBT-E, and individual CBT, for example.

Purging disorder

The treatment is often similar to that of BN. Not much is known of the outcomes, but it has been suggested that some patients may go on to develop BN or BED (Keel et al., 2019).

> Purging can be fatal, especially if there are multiple methods concurrently being used, such as vomiting, laxative abuse, or taking diuretics or diet pills. I truly believe that if I'd been given support when I was diagnosed with purging disorder, or if I'd been seen when referred again following that, that I could have avoided becoming so unwell that I was not stable enough for outpatient treatment alone and was not able to work. It was over a year before I returned to work full-time, and I feel like losing such a big chunk of my life could have been prevented.
>
> Cara Lisette

ARFID

There is limited knowledge around the evidence-based treatment for ARFID, and it isn't currently included in the NICE guidelines. ARFID care pathways are currently being reviewed by local mental health trusts, and care pathways for ARFID seem to vary depending on whether specialist eating disorder services, CAMHS (Child and Adolescent Mental Health Services), or paediatric services offer interventions and treatment. It is important to look at local commissioning arrangements to identify the treatment offered in the local area, and patients with ARFID should be referred to specialist services by their GP.

As with other eating disorders, treatment should be offered in an MDT, with family support being included where appropriate. Treatment for ARFID is usually adapted to the needs of the patient, based on the specific nature of the difficulties the person is experiencing. There will often be exploration around the underlying causes and the maintaining factors of the eating disorder.

Treatment can involve family therapy (for children and young people), CBT, and parent skills workshops, in an outpatient setting. There can be physical health concerns relating to ARFID, and it is important that treatment is aligned with the guidance from MEED (Royal College of Psychiatrists, 2022). There also needs to be consideration of the psychosocial functioning of the patient, and this needs to be supported through psychological therapy (McNaught et al., 2022).

Depending on the causes, triggers, and maintainers of the eating disorder, it is important that treatment sets individual goals, specifically:

- improving physical health
- eating a wider range of foods
- becoming less anxious eating in front of others
- becoming less fearful of choking or vomiting
- increasing interest towards food
- reducing anxiety surrounding eating.

These goals will often include repeated exposure to the circumstances and/or food types that the person is fearful of. For example, if the patient has experienced a traumatic choking incident and avoids certain foods because of this, manageable goals will be set systematically to address this avoidance, the aim being to reintroduce these foods into the person's diet.

> Therapy was very helpful with identifying new foods that might have a lower risk of being utterly abhorrent from a sensory perspective. For example, we knew that I struggled with fresh food, because it could

be slightly different each time: more bitter, sweeter, and so on. We planned that I would purchase the more expensive fruit and vegetables for a short while, to ensure the quality was as good as possible during my recovery process. We then listed fruits that were similar to the limited few that I liked, and each week planned for me to try one new one. Recovery was never forced onto me. It was my decision as to which new food I would try each week – and indeed whether I would try something new that week.

Sarah Miller

Pica

There is currently no evidence-based treatment for pica, although treatment is usually expected to involve an MDT. (Where pica is diagnosed in pregnant women, the symptoms often resolve when the baby is born. Children usually grow out of pica, especially when someone teaches them the difference between edible and non-edible items and objects.)

Psychological interventions for people experiencing pica can be offered, often including the following: mild aversion therapy, behavioural therapies, and distraction techniques.

Rumination disorder (RD)

There is currently no evidence-based treatment for RD. However, it is likely that this eating disorder will be treated in the context of an MDT. The individual needs of the patient will be assessed, and treatment offered accordingly.

Patients experiencing RD may be offered education around the condition, the mechanics of regurgitation, and the possible side effects of not controlling the disorder. To help identify if there are any emotional triggers or behaviours that contribute to RD, it may be useful to use a technique like diaphragmatic breathing, and to engage in therapy.

Living is possible and, without food, you will have no fuel to give your body the energy, vibe, and soul it needs to live. Do not restrict your life to fit into little tick boxes the professionals demand you need to fit in to gain a specific label. You should never be put in a box. The box you are put in at the end of life should come at the end of a long life, one that is fun-filled, full of achievements, love and laughter, and endless possibilities. You are not your diagnosis. Do not let it become you.

Chelsea Spencer

Medication

The NICE guidelines (NICE, 2017) suggest that medication should not be used as the sole treatment for eating disorders, and should almost always combined with psychotherapy. When medications are prescribed, careful consideration should be given to the patient's physical state, eating disorder behaviours (e.g. purging through vomiting), and side effects of medication on weight gain.

SUMMARY

- The evidence-based treatment for eating disorders is outlined in the NICE guidance (NICE, 2017).
- Early recognition and treatment for eating disorders is crucial to recovery.
- Eating disorders are fully treatable illnesses.
- There is often a multidisciplinary team involved in treating eating disorders.
- Community and outpatient treatment has the strongest evidence base for recovery and is the most common form of support offered for people with eating disorders.
- Careful medical monitoring of patients with eating disorders (who have risks around their physical health) may be required to ensure they receive enough support in the community.
- For those who require more intensive support for their physical health, an inpatient admission in a specialist eating disorder unit may be needed.
- Some patients will require treatment under the Mental Health Act, and nasogastric feeding may be implemented to preserve life.

REFERENCES

Fairburn, C. (2008). *Cognitive behaviour therapy and eating disorders*. New York: Guilford Press.

Keel, P. (2019). Purging disorders: recent advances and future challenges. *Current Opinion in Psychiatry*, 32(6), 518–524.

Lock, J., & Le Grange, D. (2012). *Treatment manual for anorexia nervosa: a family-based approach*, 2nd edition. New York: Guilford Press.

McIntosh, V. V., Jordan, J., Luty, S. E., Carter, F. A., McKenzie, J. M., Bulik, C, M, & Joyce, P. R. (2006). Specialist supportive clinical management for anorexia nervosa. *International Journal of Eating Disorders*, 39(8), 625–632. doi: 10.1002/eat.20297.

McNaught, E., Treasure, J., & Pollard, N. (2022). *Eating disorders*. Oxford: Oxford University Press.

National Centre for Collaboration in Mental Health. (2019). *Adult eating disorders: community, inpatient and day patient care – guidance for commissioners and providers*. Leeds: NHS England with Nice. www.england.nhs.uk/wp-content/uploads/2019/08/aed-guidance.pdf.

National Institute for Health and Care Excellence. (2017). *Eating disorders: recognition and treatment*. NICE guideline [NG69]. London: NICE.

Royal College of Psychiatrists. (2022). *Managing medical emergencies in eating disorders (MEED): guidance on recognition and management*. [CR233.] www.rcpsych.ac.uk/improving-care/campaigning-for-better-mental-health-policy/college-reports/2022-college-reports/cr233.

Schmidt, U., Startup, H., and Treasure, J. (2019). *A cognitive interpersonal therapy workbook for treating anorexia nervosa: the Maudsley model*. London: Routledge.

Treasure, J., Smith, G., & Crane, A. (2016) *Skills-based caring for a loved one with an eating disorder: the new Maudsley method*, 2nd edition. Hove: Routledge.

Turner, H., Bryant-Waugh, R. and Marshall, E (2015) The impact of early symptom change and therapeutic alliance on treatment outcomes in cognitive behavioural therapy for eating disorders. *Behaviour Research and Therapy*, 73, 165–169.

Waller, G., Turner, H. M., Tatham, M., Mountford, V., & Wade, T. (2019). *Brief cognitive behavioural therapy for non-underweight patients: CBT-T for eating disorders*. Abingdon: Routledge.

12

SUPPORTING SOMEONE LIVING THROUGH AN EATING DISORDER
What family and friends can do
Professor Janet Treasure

INTRODUCTION

Eating disorders develop from an interaction between genetic, developmental, and environmental factors. They may be triggered by social factors such as alienation and stress linked to minority status or problems in social adjustment. Secondary aspects of the illness serve to perpetuate the disruption to social function and allow the problem to become embedded. Families (fathers, mothers, partners, and siblings) and other close others have an important role to play by interrupting this vicious circle. However, getting help from services can be difficult, as there may be a lack of knowledge about the varying forms or stages of illness, or minimal provision.

> It is absolutely essential that we recognise that all eating disorders are serious, and all eating disorders deserve treatment and support. They do not have to be lifelong or fatal illnesses, but often can be due to a lack of provision and poor recognition of symptoms in people who are not underweight. There also needs to be more awareness and discussion around the fact that many people who struggle with their eating will cycle between different diagnoses over the course of their lifetime, and each one is as worthy of help as the next.
>
> Cara Lisette

Table 12.1 outlines the steps involved in recognising the problem, accessing, and providing help and counteracting the isolation that can maintain the disorder. This involves noticing early symptoms and signs. Assisting with help-seeking can be a complex and protracted process,

DOI: 10.4324/9781003342762-12

Table 12.1 The key stages in providing support for someone living through an eating disorder

Note early signs/symptoms	Help-seeking	Impact on the family	Provide support	Family self-care
A – Absence B – Body C – Control D – Diet E – Exercise (Pollard, 2019)	Managing the ambivalence about getting help.	Beware of the traps of accommo-dating and/or fragmenting from frustration.	Offer high-quality listening for emotional support and practical support to maintain safety and moderate risk.	Garner emotional support, e.g. information and experience. Accept practical support.

as so often the individual does not recognise that anything is wrong. The form and the prevalence of eating disorders has changed rapidly over the last 50 years. Services are overstretched and sourcing information and help to remediate the progression of the symptoms is difficult. Furthermore, the symptoms can elicit strong emotional reactions in close others, some of which inadvertently allow the symptoms to be maintained. These deplete the coping resource within the family system. High levels of stress can reduce wellbeing and isolate the family. Research has shown that the quality of life of carers/supporters of people with eating disorders is the lowest of all aspects of mental ill health.

NOTICING EARLY SYMPTOMS

It can be difficult to notice early symptoms which are often concealed or dismissed as a passing phase.

"What kind of father am I?", "How could I have let this happen?" Feelings of guilt and shame filled my mind as I looked at my 14-year-old daughter laid in a hospital bed, following an emergency admission due to the life-threatening effects of anorexia nervosa. For months, she had been restricting her food intake and exercising obsessively. But I kept hoping that this was just a passing phase. It's as if we have two boxes in our brains: one labelled "harmless" and the other "dangerous". If we see our children wearing strange clothes or listening to weird music, we put it in the "harmless" box, assuming it is just a passing phase. But if we see them experimenting with drugs, or risky

> sex, we put it in the "dangerous" box and take notice. My great mistake was to see the early stages of the eating disorder as harmless, whereas in fact they were very dangerous.
>
> Nick Pollard

Sometimes it is friends or teachers and tutors that spot the early symptoms of an eating disorder.

> It was my friends who noticed I was struggling and told the teachers at school; I was in complete denial. Part of this was because of pure fear as to what my parents would say. Coming from a Punjabi family means that there isn't much talk on mental health, and as a child we are taught anything considered "negative" can impact a family's reputation. So, I would beg my teachers not to tell my parents, but of course, for safeguarding reasons, they had to. To my surprise, it wasn't anger or shame my parents had felt, but sadness for what I had been enduring alone.
>
> Anjali Heer

HOW CAN CLOSE OTHERS RECOGNISE EARLY SYMPTOMS AND SIGNS?

Parents are usually closely involved in the presentation and management of avoidant restrictive food intake disorder (ARFID), pica, and rumination disorder, which usually have their onset in childhood. However, sometimes families accommodate these eating difficulties, and it is only later in life that the individual becomes aware of the social disruption caused by their eating difficulties and seeks help for themselves.

Detecting early anorexia nervosa

Anorexia nervosa (AN) classically emerges early in adolescence when the individual is dependent on the family. However, the onset can be insidious and sometimes dismissed by health professionals as a passing phase or treated as a form of gastrointestinal upset. The individual themselves may not notice anything wrong and may perceive that aspects of the illness have benefits. In the first descriptions of AN, one characteristic noted by physicians was that patients protested they did not suffer and therefore nothing was wrong. Indeed, people with

AN are often noted to be energetic and overactive. In addition, some of the consequence of weight loss (such as suppression of emotions) may be valued or align with personality functioning, such as the preference for rigid rules and certainty (see Chapter 2).

Although there may be signs associated with AN that may signal to others that all is not well, food and eating may not always be an overt signal, as the trigger may be negative energy balance caused by an increased amount of exercise rather than a reduction in eating.

> As she was studying hard and the exercise was part of her study programme, I think I ignored the fact she was doing so much, for a lot longer than I felt comfortable with.
>
> Chris Avenell

The presentation may be complex and harder to detect if it is associated with comorbidities such as depression, anxiety, obsessive compulsive symptoms, and autistic spectrum traits, or physical problems such as diabetes and hypermobility. Delays in the early recognition and diagnosis of eating disorders prevent the opportunity to benefit from early intervention.

Detecting early binge spectrum disorder

Binge spectrum disorders usually develop later in adolescence or early adult life. The symptoms can be shrouded in secrecy or not recognised as part of an illness, but seen as moral failings. The emotional aspects of the disorder may dominate the presentation, whereas the eating symptoms remain as shameful secrets which are not disclosed to others. Indeed, fewer than 20 per cent of people with binge spectrum disorders present for treatment for their eating problems, although they may present to services with psychological (depression, anxiety) or physical symptoms (type 2 diabetes, obesity). Also, they may have presented in childhood with symptoms of attention deficit hyperactivity disorder (ADHD).

The changing profile of disordered eating can make recognising a diagnosis difficult. Many of the concerns about body shape and eating expressed in people with binge spectrum disorders are widely shared amongst adolescents and it can be difficult to determine when the symptoms have crossed a diagnostic threshold, leading to an entrenched pattern of behaviours and an impaired quality of life. The Family Mental Wealth eating disorders ABCDE tool (Absence, Body, Control, Diet, Exercise;

Pollard, 2019), included in each clinical chapter of this book, outlines some of the signs and symptoms that may alert others to the problem.

HOW CAN CLOSE OTHERS PROMOTE HELP-SEEKING?

The next step involves information-gathering, knowing how to help and avoid hindering recovery by falling into traps such as accommodating the illness. The recent inclusion of eating disorders in diagnostic manuals means that there has been a lack of information about eating disorders and a lack of services to match the changing epidemiology (Chapter 2).

People with lived experience can be a bridge towards getting help, as well as a source of information. Also, many charities are available to provide help such as FEAST and BEAT. The role of close others in facilitating help-seeking varies according to the diagnosis and age of onset, and is not always straightforward.

> Absolutely nothing prepares you for what comes after diagnosis, but the more knowledge you have, the more empowered you feel. And that feeds hope.
>
> Rochelle Rouse

THE IMPACT OF EATING DISORDERS ON THE FAMILY AND CLOSE OTHERS

Various aspects of an eating disorder have an impact on close others. All forms of eating disorder can be associated with a withdrawal from social eating. This can disrupt family function, as sharing meals is a key component of social functioning. However, in modern times the importance of this has become eroded, and some suggest that this may have led to the increase in eating disorders.

The overt signs of starvation in the restricting forms of eating disorders, and the reluctance to follow the logical advice to "just eat", can elicit strong and mixed emotions in close others. Interactions vary over time and with the type of relationship, parental, partner, sibling, or friend. A common parental response is to become anxious, with a strong urge to "fix" the problem and to protect the individual from harm. These reactions are so automatic and universal, and we have found it helpful to use animal metaphors to describe and manage them, as a means of stepping back.

Anxiety, accommodating (kangaroo, overprotective response)

Anxiety, a common emotional consequence in caregivers and part of the genetic predisposition to develop an eating disorder, can provoke close others to develop an overprotective, kangaroo approach. This involves providing reassurance and making allowances and accommodating eating disorder behaviours. These can dominate family life and include buying low-calorie items, cooking without oil, monopolising the kitchen, not participating in family meals, or taking a long time to eat and/or undertaking compensatory behaviours such as ritualised and solitary exercise.

Accommodation is an understandable and natural parental response to an anxious child, especially if it is associated with emotional dysregulation such as irritability. However, accommodating behaviours may allow eating disorder behaviours to become more accepted and embedded. Second, these behaviours disturb family function, and other family members may resent the disruption and impact of these behaviours on their lives. Counter-reactions ranging from irritation through to hostility may serve to fragment family support and isolate the individual with an eating disorder. Accommodating/overprotective behaviours such as replacing missing food or providing money to buy food, can develop because of binge eating. Again, these may allow the behaviours to continue.

Frustration (rhino and jellyfish response)

The frustration caused by the various strategies to avoid eating or to compensate for eating can lead to anger and assertive responses. These can clash with some of the accommodating behaviours described above and cause fragmentation within the family. The symptoms of binge eating and purging are usually secretive activities. However, when they are noticed (e.g. mess in the bathroom or kitchen, disappearance of money and/or food), they can elicit anger and disgust in others. A vicious circle can develop, as binge eating is triggered by negative emotions.

Calibration and competition

Another pattern of interaction that may develop within close relationships arises from a form of calibration or competition with the behaviours. For example, the individual living with an eating disorder may buy, prepare, and encourage other family members to eat to excess foods that they themselves abstain from, or compete by increasing exercise and hence energy expenditure. During meal support, close others may be expected to match their eating behaviour with that of the individual on a recovery diet.

Stepping back from unhelpful patterns of interaction

These mixed and extreme interactions with close others can damage family harmony and are difficult to disentangle. Information about how to support someone with an eating disorder is available from services and the charitable sector (see the list at the end of the chapter). For the most part, this support is directed at parents, but siblings and partners can have relationship problems which may need a more personalised approach.

Accommodating behaviour and other reactions associated with high levels of emotional dysregulation can lead to depression, anxiety, stress, and burden – in both the person with an eating disorder and the support system. One of the first steps that supporters need to take is to optimise their wellbeing by sourcing and utilising emotional and practical support (see below in support for supporters). Not only can this be good for themselves, but it can also be of help to the individual with an eating disorder by setting an example of how to utilise effective strategies for emotional regulation and stress management.

IMPACT ON THE FAMILY/CARERS

Although for the most part it is parents, especially mothers, who take on the main caring role, in older patients it may be that partners or siblings who contribute to this role. The impact on partners and older siblings can differ from those with a parental role. For example it is common for partners to report on the loneliness they often experience, as the only carer in their family unit.

I first met my wife quite early into her recovery from eating disorders ... It would be fair to say that I experienced times of feeling distant and intentionally alienated by her during those early days ...

She did the hard work internally, and I was simply a loving constant, walking with her as she continued her path ... Although it was sometimes hard, we always maintained an atmosphere where communication without anger, frustration, or judgment was possible. Patience and listening with loving understanding were the keys to us coming through to the other side of eating disorders.

David Griffiths

Siblings offer the possibility of one of the longest relationships throughout life. They often notice the early symptoms, but get confused about what is happening. They can experience a complex mix of emotions — including sadness, anger, jealousy, and competition — and may feel helpless in supporting the family, feeling paralysed and unable to access help themselves because they do not want to tell tales outside the family. In child and adolescent services where forms of family treatment are used, they may be asked to be involved in treatment. Adult siblings over time may be drawn into providing the lead carer role. Research into the complex interaction between the impact of the illness on siblings themselves and the supportive role that is possible is only now emerging (Piekunka et al., 2023).

Having a sibling with an eating disorder is somewhat of a journey, and there are different stages and feelings along the way. I remember at first, disbelief. You reach for your limited knowledge on the subject and all I knew at the time was what happened to Karen Carpenter. I naively thought that her illness was due to the pressures of show business, so how could it be happening to my sister? Eating is such a natural part of life that it felt impossible that this could be a problem.

There were some tough times as a family. I could see the pain my mother was feeling, the desperate want to help, mixed with helplessness. At a particularly low time, I remember my parents needed a break and they went away, but not too far. I was home to keep an eye on my sister, but it was simply too overwhelming for me, and I had to call my parents back.

I had never seen anything like it in my life — it felt like her eating disorder had reached an almost industrialised scale.

In hindsight, I never felt that I was particularly supportive, I didn't delve into the psychology or attend any meetings, but I have to remember that I was a child, too. Perhaps the role of a sibling is to just be there, not judging, commenting, or interfering. Combining this with their constant love and support, it could be exactly what is needed.

Stephen Parish

When my sister got ill, it was a very confusing time for everyone; the immediate family seemed to close in on itself. We all wanted to do whatever we could to help her, but there was no one to advise us on how to do this. I didn't know who I could turn to for help and advice, because it didn't feel like it was my story to tell.

Anya Heneghan

Task sharing and active support

The form and content of caregiving needs to be personalised and adapted to match the developmental stage and the evolution of the illness. One of the first steps for carers is to recognise which of the common reactions to the illness described above may have started to dominate family functioning and to take steps to have a coherent, consistent approach, avoiding some of the extremes depicted in the animal metaphors.

Caregivers of young adolescents with a recent onset of illness may be actively involved in supporting change through planning, supporting, and reflecting on progress of providing meal support. Family-based therapy which is based on these principles is an evidence-based approach that can support those with a short duration of illness (Fisher et al., 2019; see Chapter 11).

For adults with a later and/or or more protracted illness, other strategies to involve the family in treatment may be needed. Although direct meal support may not be possible, the family can contribute to resilience and recovery in many other ways. For example, they can hold the important memory of the evolving, pre-eating-disorder identity and help their loved reclaim this aspect of themselves. Families can provide the resources and optimism to allow for a return to that developmental trajectory.

When in adolescent services, we were asked about our daughter, her likes/dislikes, etc. in life. However, once in adult services, we very rarely got to meet anyone directly involved in her care and have never been asked about our daughter's pre-life before an eating disorder – might have been useful, I think! Now so entrenched with anorexia – my daughter's pre-anorexic personality is almost a forgotten trait – very occasionally I get a rare glimpse, a slight smile, a brief memory of years gone by, which reminds me: my daughter is still in there somewhere.

Nicky Smith

Some treatments for adults with anorexia nervosa specifically include carers – for example, in the Maudsley model for anorexia nervosa treatment in adults (MANTRA), the patient cognitive inter-personal workbook (Schmidt et al., 2019) has a section for support-ers that includes information on how to provide both psychological and physical support and describes how to avoid common traps. Moreover, supplementary materials in the form of books, videos, and websites co-developed with people with lived experience provide more in-depth information and skills-sharing tips (Langley et al., 2019; Macdonald, 2021; Pollard, 2019; Treasure et al., 2016). Other websites are shown at the end of this chapter.

The supporter's role varies depending on the level of ambivalence and readiness to change, the level of parental responsibility (which depends on age and level of risk), whether the focus is on under- or over-nutrition, and whether comorbidity is present. In contrast to accommodating, which is a common reaction to undereating, close others may get drawn into taking a more active nagging and/or arguing stance to counter episodes of loss of control overeating. The aim is to establish a balanced form of support, with help from others to recognise these traps.

The next step is to plan a joint strategy to withdraw gradually from repeated patterns of unhelpful interactions. In the first instance, this needs to be discussed and agreed between key supporters. Next, the plan should be introduced in conversation with the individual with an eating disorder, who may protest about what they see as a with-drawal of support. Coming up with a plan may take several conversa-tions (listening breaks), after which it may be helpful to follow up with a written summary and an agreement to monitor and calibrate progress on a regular basis.

> For someone was starting this journey, I would say get educated … The fact that my daughter didn't rapidly gain weight and it was a slow, slow, slow, process wasn't because I was failing. An eating disorder is different in every child; how they recover and respond varies hugely for lots of complex reasons. It *is* your job as a parent, though, to keep hope alive. Surround yourself with a support network who will help you do this. You can't do it alone. Your child needs to see that you believe in recovery, and your job is to walk with them until they can see it for themselves.
>
> Rochelle Rouse

I would say to a carer, at the beginning of this awful journey trust your instinct, not the person you are supporting. The illness will make them lie to you. It's not them lying, it's the illness so trust your instinct.

Chris Avenell

1. Remember you will never win an argument with anorexia.
2. Think very carefully what to say before you say anything at all.
3. Use patience by the bucket-load.
4. Take control over the diet from day one – be strict, don't accept excuses, and change whatever mealtime plan you had made.
5. It's OK to be suspicious. Check those pockets, watch and support after a meal, don't believe what you are told. Be firm but fair.
6. Set out plans and boundaries together.

Nicky Smith

Carer support skills

We use animal metaphors to illustrate helpful caregiver skills. For example, a dolphin approach represents a wise, hands-off, nudging, style, expressing warmth with a small smile. An allied style to this is that of a St Bernard dog, providing warmth and support in a cold and risky environment, and keeping calm to avoid provoking avalanches. Finally, the elephant approach involves a trunk–to–tail, wise, and cooperative approach between a network of supporters (professional and lay).

In the early days, I had an image in my mind. It felt as if the family was in a rowing boat, struggling against the current of a fast-flowing river, to get to a place called "My daughter is well again". And I felt that my role, as the dad, was to get us there. So, I was rowing really hard, and so was my wife and other family members. And then I looked round, and there she was rowing in the opposite direction. So, I got frustrated. But then, one day, I suddenly realised that I had got the wrong goal. My job was not to "Get us up the river to that place where my daughter is well again'" Only she could do that. My role was to keep us all together in the boat. So that we could encourage her, support her, and help her as she made progress on her recovery journey. I couldn't make her well again, but I could keep us all together in the boat.

Nick Pollard

High-quality listening to explore the uncertainties and confusion that are part of an eating disorder are essential to untangle the complexities. Open questions, which are driven by curiosity not by an adversarial "yes or no" answer, are best. We are not suggesting that family members need to become therapists. However, skilful listening breaks underpinned by some knowledge of an eating disorder can be invaluable.

A key part of listening is to demonstrate that you are attending, by attempting to reflect what you thought was said. Good listening may involve thinking pauses to reflect on what was said, what was heard, and to check out what was meant. (Perfection is not needed. Indeed, tolerating making errors is a helpful therapeutic tool!) "Every mistake is a treasure" is a useful adage to use in work with people with an eating disorder. This level of processing means that the flow is different to standard family exchanges.

> By asking open questions and using reflective listening, I gradually gained insight into what the anorexia felt like for her. I began to understand the intense anxiety and guilt she experienced when she faced food or couldn't exercise. Gradually, I discovered how I could use non-directive coaching skills to help her refocus her mind upon her life goals. As she says, I changed from leading her on, to cheering her on. I couldn't fight the illness for her. I had to love her, believe in her, and help her to believe in herself again.
>
> Nick Pollard

Listening breaks should be held on a regular basis, at a time and place to minimise interruptions. Some people find that listening breaks might be held on the move, driving, taking the dog for a walk, etc. However, these may limit the number of participants and may get interrupted. These conversations do not need to be protracted; Bill Miller, an expert on this form of support, says that five minutes of good-quality listening provides a great deal of help. If possible, a proportion these high-quality listening breaks should occur with all members of the support system.

Be open to listen to contrasting agendas

As discussed earlier, it is common for people with undereating disorders such as AN and ARFID to conceptualise the illness as a solution to, and not a cause of, problems. Therefore, they do not perceive themselves to have the motivation or ability to change. This lack of motivation may be because aspects of the eating disorder may be valued, because it fits with parts of the personality and can provide short-term benefits. For example, AN may be associated with:

- a means of avoiding feared events
- an alignment with traits in which order and certainty are valued
- more attention from close others
- reduced hostility from others
- reduced expectations to self and others
- arrested maturation delaying facing the uncertainty about an independent identity (in terms of values, sexuality, or gender, etc.).

Thus, the content of the conversation in listening breaks might centre around the pros and cons of changing, and a consideration of the pros and cons of not changing. The conversation is elaborated by moving the time window back and forth in time, and from self to others.

Moving to solution-based conversations

When there are mixed feelings about change, it is useful to structure the conversation around a ladder of readiness. For example, the following questions can be used to derive a readiness score from a ruler scaled from 0 (no readiness to change) and 10 (high readiness). The following solution-based questions can be applied to many facets of eating disorder behaviours (further details about this strategy can be obtained from *Caring for a Loved One with an Eating Disorder*, Langley et al., 2019):

- What, specifically, could you do to get started?
- What, specifically, would you like to be different?
- If the first step is successful, then what?
- Who else could you ask for support, assistance, if anyone?
- What could you ask for?
- What would be signs that things are going well?
- How would you know if you were off-track?
- What would you do if you got off-track?

EMOTIONALLY INTELLIGENT CONVERSATIONS

Problems with managing emotions are common within all eating disorders. Therefore, special attention is needed to attend and reflect on emotions which may be muted in AN, or strong, overpowering, and confusing in those with binge spectrum disorders. The acronym "ALVS" describes a reflecting tool, developed as part of the toolkit of emotion-focused therapy for carers (Lafrance et al., 2020). The following are useful steps to follow to build emotionally intelligent conversations:

- *Attend*
  Notice, and gently and curiously reflect on both verbal and non-verbal emotional signals.
- *Label*
  Reflect on your interpretation of the emotion. For example, it looks as if you are frightened. (It does not matter if you get it wrong! You can be hesitant. Any first step to untangle complex emotions and interpersonal reactions can be helpful.)
- *Validate*
  Generate a hypothesis using *because*. You felt sad *because* Y let you down by/when X … Perhaps, you can have two or three *because* comments (remember that scientists use hypotheses as signposts, and rejecting a hypothesis is as useful as having one proved).
- *Support*
  It makes me want to give you a hug (what might mitigate the emotion?).

OTHER SUPPORTIVE RELATIONSHIPS

Often, support from people with lived experience of an eating disorder throughout the recovery journey is extremely helpful. This may be in the form of face-to-face peer mentoring, which many services and charities are providing, or accessing some of the many written or recorded materials (Bryant, 2021). Task sharing with people with lived experience has been widely used for AN and has the potential to be usefully applied to the wider spectrum of people with eating problems.

Friends can also provide support if you are open about the problem.

Specific to food, again, it's all about communicating (and showing you are open to communication) what works best for each individual. For example, I find it useful to have friends do little things like ask me if I've eaten, if we want to eat together, or if I'd prefer to hang out in a non-food setting – but, for others, this could be triggering and they don't want to discuss food at all.

Marina

SUPPORT FOR SUPPORTERS

Finally is the need to source practical and emotional support for all members of the support team themselves, as this can be an exhausting, isolating, and frightening role. Unfortunately, the quality of life for all involved is poor. Carers may benefit from confiding in friends or family or accessing a support group. However, people with an eating disorder may have commanded the family not to tell others about their difficulties. While it is understandable not to want confidential aspects of the illness to be discussed in depth, getting support from others is one of the most effective ways of regulating emotional distress. Therefore, families may need to discuss why and how they should accommodate this request. Accessing practical support from others, such as helping you in the garden, looking after pets, perhaps making a meal for the family, is less problematic. This may allow caregivers to spend time on other family activities. Family members should be offered a needs assessment, and different treatment may be offered.

> My husband and I had some therapy after I recovered, to reflect on the impact my eating disorder had on our relationship, and that was helpful for both of us. We'd both say that it's equally important for the partner of an eating disorder sufferer to have someone to talk to openly as much as the sufferer.
>
> Christina Taylor

CONCLUSION

Isolation has been recognised to be a key consequence and causation of a protracted course of an eating disorder (McKnight & Boughton, 2009). Close others can buffer this problem through promoting an early access to treatment and by providing a network of emotional and practical support. In this chapter, we have described the common traps that can derail help provided from others, and briefly outlined the steps that can promote recovery. Supporters play an enormous role by holding the hope in recovery. This is always possible, no matter how protracted and severe the illness, and how many cycles of inpatient rescue might be needed.

My relationship with both my daughters now is wonderful! From our relationship being hugely damaged during the days when we were in crisis, to my eldest daughter screaming she hated me and to just give up on her and let her die, we now have the most loving relationship.

Suzanne Baker

SUMMARY

- Close others may play an important role by spotting early signs and symptoms of an eating disorder and facilitating help-seeking.
- The social support network for people with an eating disorder has an important role in reducing the duration of untreated illness, and their support can improve outcomes.
- Problems with eating disrupt social functioning and can lead to exasperation or accommodating interactions. These can cause fragmentation within the family and allow eating disorder symptoms to persist.
- It is now recognised that involving close others in treatment, in a way that is developmentally appropriate, can improve outcomes.
- People with lived experience can provide an invaluable additional form of support.

REFERENCES

Bryant, E. (2021). Anorexia: the great taboo. *The Lancet Psychiatry*, 8(10), 866–867.

Fisher, C. A., Skocic, S., Rutherford, K. A., & Hetrick, S. E. (2019). Family therapy approaches for anorexia nervosa. *Cochrane Database of Systematic Reviews*, 5(5). doi:10.1002/14651858.CD004780.pub3.

Lafrance, A., Henderson, K. A., & Mayan, S. (2020). *Emotion-focused family therapy: a transdiagnostic model for caregiver-focused interventions*. Washington, DC: American Psychological Association.

Langley, J., Todd, G., & Treasure, J. (2019). *Caring for a loved one with an eating disorder: he New Maudsley skills-based training manual*. Abingdon: Routledge.

Macdonald, P. (2021). *How to help someone with an eating disorder: a practical handbook*. London: Welbeck Balance.

McKnight, R., & Boughton, N. (2009). Anorexia nervosa. *British Medical Journal*, 339. doi: https://doi.org/10.1136/bmj.b3800.

Piekunka, K., Dimitropoulos, G., Treasure, J., Singh, M., Whitlow, B., & Tan, J. (2023). Siblings and eating disorders. In P. Robinson et al. (eds), *Eating disorders: an international comprehensive view*, 1–19. Edinburgh: Springer Cham. https://doi.org/10.1007/978-3-030-97416-9.

Pollard, N. J. (2019). The ABCDE tool for spotting the early signs of an eating disorder. *The Family Files*, 4. FamilyMentalWealth.com/FamilyFiles.

Schmidt, U., Startup, H., & Treasure, J. (2019). *A cognitive interpersonal therapy workbook for treating anorexia nervosa: the Maudsley model*. London: Routledge.

Treasure, J., Smith, G., & Crane, A. (2016). *Skills-based caring for a loved one with an eating disorder: the new Maudsley method*, 2nd edition. Hove: Routledge.

Additional sources of information and support

- www.beateatingdisorders.org.uk
- https://familymentalwealth.com/families/
- www.feast-ed.org

LETTERS OF HOPE
Edited by Jess Griffiths

INTRODUCTION

Journeying through an eating disorder can sometimes be very hard, but full recovery is always possible. This chapter is written by people who have lived experience of an eating disorder. The voices of those who have lived with eating disorders or supported someone with an eating disorder offer powerful reflections and motivation to "keep going" and not lose hope that recovery is achievable. The first section of the chapter is written as "letters of hope", offering motivation and powerful insight to keep going on the road of recovery. The second section is also written by people with lived experience, offering advice about journeying through the process.

LETTERS OF HOPE

Anjali Heer – lived experience of other specified feeding or eating disorder

Dear friend,

I heard you were struggling lately, and I know telling you it's all going to be OK is something that you've probably heard many times before and something you may not even believe right now. I know you may think that I don't know how it feels to have a constant battle in your mind over food, weight, and the way you look, or that I have never felt so hopeless of recovery, so I won't try and convince you. Instead, I'll tell you something else.

You are strong.

No one chooses to have an eating disorder, but you can choose recovery. There is strength in the choice you've made and your commitment to try. Despite the setbacks recently, with each breath you take and each

DOI: 10.4324/9781003342762-13

foot forward to take a step you will move forward and make it through today. That in itself is something you should be proud of.

There is a future beyond the pain you are feeling right now; you just have to give yourself the chance to see that future through choosing to keep moving forward. There is growth in the uncomfortable that you are feeling right now. Through creating new habits and doing things you've never done before, it will be hard. But remember you would rather choose the hardship of recovery, and seeing a better life at the end of it, than surrendering to a voice in your head that isn't even yours and prevents you from living that life and being that person you want.

I want to remind you of that hope and your strength in choosing to hold onto it. I want to remind you that you are worth recovery and that you are beautiful and that you are powerful, and the moment you recognise that is the same moment you will realise how far you've come just by taking one small step at a time, each day.

I believe in you. It's time you believe in you, too.

Endless amounts of love and healing,
Your friend,
Anjali

Adam Fare – lived experience of neurodiversity and otherwise specified feeding eating disorder

When we talk about recovery, often it is talked about in very simple ways. I 100 per cent believe that everyone can recover, no matter how long you've been struggling for, or how unwell you've been. However, that recovery will look different for everyone, and it is about finding your best quality of life given your circumstances.

Recovery isn't a body size, it isn't a look, it isn't a specific meal plan, and yours will look different to everyone else's. That doesn't mean you've failed; it means you've succeeded in finding your best quality of life, your happiness, and your health.

You are an amazing, unique person.

Jess Sharman – lived experience of other specified feeding or eating disorder

Dear anyone struggling with an eating disorder,

It's not easy to know how to start this letter. There are so many things I want to say, that I want you to know, that initially my mind goes blank. Not only that – when I start to write, I can hear that creeping voice of perfectionism trying to sneak in, telling me that my flow is off, or that my letter isn't "good enough". And that's not too dissimilar from what I remember my eating disorder being like: that constant voice of self-criticism, always telling me that I wasn't good enough no matter what I said or did. But what is different now is that I'm able to sit here, write this letter, and say that voice is wrong. I am enough. And simply saying a little bit of what I've learned during recovery could be valuable to someone struggling like I was before.

So here I am. And I guess the first thing I want to say is that recovery is possible. Yes, even for you. There's been many times where I've felt stuck, hopeless even. And it's perfectly OK to feel that way – sometimes, you're so consumed by your emotions or by your eating disorder that it's hard to see any other way forward. But the truth is, these moments are temporary. They sometimes don't feel it, but they are. Yes, there will be tough times ahead, days when recovery feels so, so difficult. But there will be other days when you're laughing with friends or family, perhaps even having a meal together, and you'll be doing things that your eating disorder previously stopped you from doing. And you'll be present! You'll actually be able to stay with the beauty of that moment and feel that genuine connection with your loved ones. And there will be days when you can just enjoy a nice walk in the sun, stopping now and then to admire the world around you. And there will be days when you're doing what you love – whether it's a hobby, immersing yourself in a great film, volunteering, or doing a job you love ... And on those days recovery will be worth it.

And I guess part of all this is finding what is actually meaningful to *you*. Finding who you are, away from the eating disorder. I used to think my eating disorder consumed me. It was a huge part of my identity and I didn't know who I was without it. However, the truth is, you are so, so many things. You are someone's child, son, or daughter. You might be someone's sibling, friend, partner. You might be a parent, or become a parent one day. You are all your values, hopes, and dreams. You are your hobbies and interests. You are all your feelings – the comfortable and uncomfortable ones. You are your beliefs and personality. So, I guess the next message I want to share is that your eating disorder, if anything, is just a part of you – don't forget about the rest.

So, I really recommend trying to find what you love and what gives you that sense of meaning and purpose. And then use that to drive your recovery. That's what I did – without even realising it at the time! And it is something I continue to do, whenever there's a difficult moment or any eating-disorder-related thoughts try to creep in (including that pesky perfectionism!), I remind myself of what's important to me. And I ask myself, "How do I want to be?" And the answer always aligns with recovery, and my continued personal growth.

You are enough, you are worthy, recovery is possible. So, go ahead and make recovery your own.

Lots of love,
Someone who's living her recovery x

Christina Taylor – lived experience of anorexia nervosa

If you're reading this and struggling, I hope I can offer you some comfort and light in the darkest times. I've had an eating disorder since I was 13. It doesn't define me, but it's part of who I am. Whenever I meet someone else with an eating disorder, no matter the type, it often feels like you speak a secret language that only those who have been there understand. I hope this letter speaks to you in that way.

If you'd told me 12 years ago that I would have two beautiful healthy children and I would be at peace with myself, eating what I choose and free of purging, I could never have believed you. My life was entirely ruled by routine, self-medication with alcohol to allow myself to eat anything at all, and rigidity.

Last week, I stood up in front of 80 people in a new workplace I'd been in for less than a month and spoke about my recovery journey. When I started in the world of work, I lied and was so deeply ashamed of my illness. I would have done anything to hide who I really was. My recovery allowed me to hold myself accountable and help others along this difficult path.

My recovery was not overnight. There were many failed attempts and struggles, disappointments in myself, and anger at a treatment system that didn't seem to understand me. One day I committed to a life without anorexia, but the next day I woke up and it was still there. One thing I have learned about my eating disorder is the reality of "black and white" thinking and I attributed this to recovery and body image along with everything else. Either I was recovered – I loved my body, could eat whatever I wanted – or I was anorexic.

Wrestling control back from my eating disorder meant learning to accept a level of compromise (or mediocrity, as my critical inner voice deemed it). I didn't wake every morning at ultimate peace with my body and food – in fact, some days I didn't like it at all. It was in how I began to address this. I learned that the feelings of hatred I directed at myself were often a way of numbing myself from things I simply didn't want to feel. Focusing on my body or the calories in a different type of bread prevented me from feeling hurt or stressed. Starting to unpick what these feelings meant beginning to ease how I felt about food. I began to accept that how I felt was how everyone else felt – some days good, some days bad. Did I really need to be exceptional and different in the ways I wanted to be? Probably not. Being normal was actually what I'd always dreamed of, and I didn't need to restrict or make myself sick to achieve that, either.

I started to challenge the deep-rooted beliefs I had that eating certain things would lead to ultimate chaos and disaster. That I'd totally lose control of my body and never be able to get it back. The reality was, of course, that what I got back was my life. I started to think more rationally, to contextualise the thoughts that made sense when I was at the height of my anorexia, but actually have zero factual basis or scientific grounding.

I stopped believing my body was somehow different to everyone else's, and began accepting that I couldn't always be the best at everything I wanted to be. I started teaching my children that, too!

Recovery was liked climbing Everest with no training at the start. I cried over everything and it felt that I would never ever see a world which wasn't entirely underpinned by my illness. A wonderful therapist said to me at the start of my work that if it felt hard, it meant it was working and I committed to that, seeing each challenge as a step away from my eating disorder, no matter how impossible it felt. As my recovery progressed, it stopped becoming an effort at all. One day, I realised I was doing the things I'd have been working towards for months without even thinking about it at all. I was simply happy and my life had started to take centre stage instead of my illness. That was when I felt I'd truly recovered and the almost two decades of struggling were behind me.

Ultimately, I want to tell you that, no matter how hard you find things now, whether you are at the beginning, middle, or end of a journey, there will be a point in which you make that turning to leaving your eating disorder behind you, where the challenges are welcome instead of awful, because going back is so much worse. I struggled for 17 years, the kind of patient that many clinicians might give up on, but the day came where I was able to recover, and not just recover, but share my story in places like this. Never give up hope.

> One day I committed to a life without anorexia, but the next day I woke up and it was still there.

Kirsty Stapledon – lived experience of bulimia nervosa

This letter is to you. The you that is having a rough week. The you that currently sees nothing but darkness. The you that doesn't feel worthy. The you that can't bear to look in the mirror. The you that feels inadequate. The you that blames yourself for every mistake or everything that goes wrong. I see you – I feel your pain, I have sat in the darkness where you are now, feeling completely alone. I understand your struggles. I understand that your eating disorder isn't your choice. I know it convinces you that this is all you have. But I am here to tell you that you are enough.

You aren't broken; you are brave. I know it is scary, but you are strong. I know you are exhausted, but today is not your forever. I am here to hold hope for you, in the times where you may not be able to hold it for yourself. I can reassure you that it does get better. You have time. You have potential and make this world a better place by just existing. You can recover. Recovery isn't just the absence of the eating disorder. Recovery is finding meaning and joy again. Recovery is in the small moments and milestones. Recovery is:

- **R**ediscovering yourself, personality, and hobbies again.
- **E**very new friend you're yet to make.
- **C**reating new memories in all the new places you're yet to explore.
- **O**rdering food in or spontaneous meals out without guilt.
- **V**aluing enjoyment over food, numbers, and exercise.
- **E**nergy to achieve your goals and ambitions.
- **R**ealising your body is not your worth.
- **Y**our confidence, strength, and self-worth growing.

Nay Parnell – lived experience of anorexia nervosa and "diabetes burnout"

Dear Warrior,

I know recovery feels impossible at times. I know you feel broken beyond repair and exhausted from the fight, and that you don't have the strength to beat this. But let me tell you that those feelings don't reflect the truth.

Recovery is hard, yes. But it's always possible. I strongly believe that every single person can recover, no matter the length or severity of your eating disorder. Nobody is beyond help, not even you. So, however hopeless and lost you feel, recovery truly is possible for you.

It's not your fault that you find yourself here. You don't deserve this pain or the punishment the eating disorder puts you through. And, although you might feel entwined with it right now, you are not your eating disorder.

Recovery isn't about trying to change yourself; it's simply the willingness to challenge the eating disorder. When you have that willingness to prove the eating disorder wrong, you are already winning. You'll see that it's a liar. And every time you challenge an eating disorder thought, belief, and behaviour, the stronger you'll become.

You might not think you've got what it takes to beat this, but trust me when I say that if you can live with an eating disorder, then you definitely have the strength and resilience to overcome it.

Even a tiny step forward is still progress, so every little victory is worth celebrating. You are worth fighting for and, while there is still breath in your lungs, you can keep choosing recovery – you can and will beat this.

I confidently believe in you, as does everyone else who is living out their recovery. We are rooting for you and celebrating every win with you.

Love,
Nay Parnell xx

If you can live with an eating disorder, then you definitely have the strength and resilience to overcome it.

Dave Chawner – lived experience of anorexia nervosa

Dear [younger] Dave,

I'm writing to you from the future ... but don't worry, that's not as spooky as it sounds. It's more of a *Bill & Ted's Excellent Adventure* vibe I'm going for, rather than *Terminator* or *Donnie Darko*.

I've written and rewritten this about 14 times, but I've decided I'm never going to be able to get it perfect, which is actually one of the biggest lessons you need to learn, mate. It's all well and good striving for the absolute best, and that's commendable. However, you need to tone it down a bit, mate. There's only so much you can control, so control the controllables.

Does that make any sense?

What I mean is, I've heard things are a bit rubbish right now. And I know there are days you feel that more than others. And, on those days you don't feel it so much, you try and tell yourself everything is now all hunky-dory. But I wanted to give you a little nudge in the right direction, a little helping hand. Remember that documentary you watched recently and how you began talking to people about mental health?

That was really good, mate. But you've gotta understand: there is mental health as well as mental illness. And, yeah, I know there were some unhelpful comments, but look at it this way ...

The difference between emotions and mental health is like the difference between the weather and the climate. So, your emotions are like the weather, they change three, four, or maybe more, times a day. Up to a point, that's normal. However, your mental health is your mental climate. It should be generally sunny, warm, dry. The odd rainy day helps things to grow. But, when it's always blowing a gale, raining, and freezing, that isn't an environment where everything can flourish.

Why am I telling you this?

Well, your mental climate is shifting, mate. It's gone from summer to a pretty deep winter. And you think that the way to deal with that is to focus on food, calories, exercising, and chasing that fleeting moment of stepping on the scales and seeing the number drop. If you keep chasing that dragon, mate, it's only gonna drag you deeper. That ain't the solution.

And, people have started to notice, right? They've begun to ask questions. And, every time they do, there's that weird sting of embarrassment, but also guilty pride. Believe me, mate, the "road to ruin" isn't all Hollywood's cracked it up to be. It might seem all "rock and roll", but that just sells movies, mate. The reality is really awful, and really dull. Like, properly boring. Like, so boring it makes Geography lessons look like an acid trip at Glasto. So, do yourself a favour: stop an issue before it becomes a problem.

You'll keep saying, "I'll get help when ..." But that moment never comes, mate. You'll always shift the goalposts. Start now. Right now. Today. Read up about "eating disorders" and realise that they are a spectrum rather than something you "have" and "don't have"; they are serious and it ain't gonna give you the answers you're looking for.

I can't tell you what's coming ahead (I've seen *Dr Who* and all that sci-fi crap, and I know, if I begin to give you spoilers, then it'll rip the time-space continuum apart and Uncle Rich will become a Dalek), but all I will say is ... don't let things get worse before you can get better. That is the thief of time, mate, and you'll only regret it.

Look, I've probably said too much already. I've gotta go before I shout my mouth off too much and time and space begins crumbling.

Take care, mate ... and I mean that.

Dave
P.S. Don't take Maths at A level – you're rubbish at it!

SUPPORT AND ADVICE FROM PEOPLE WITH LIVED EXPERIENCE

Florence Greenwood – lived experience of anorexia nervosa

Advice I'd give to others starting out on their recovery journey.

- Take each day as it comes.
- Don't focus always on the destination, but on the journey and small wins you're having along the way.
- Don't be hard on yourself! Appreciate that setbacks are part of recovery. Setbacks are important lessons we need in order to move forward. Success is an accumulation of many failures.
- Keep reminding yourself this is possible, especially when it feels too hard. People recover from eating disorders. And you can, too.
- Think what your authentic identity is and start filling your time with things that embody this identity. As you progress in your recovery, a gap will start to open up, as anorexia shrinks. It's important to fill that space with meaning and purpose, so there is no room for anorexia to come back in.

There is an analogy I wrote called "the boat and lighthouse", visually explaining how it felt to be recovering from anorexia.

I'm sailing on a small boat alone. It's nighttime. It's always nighttime. It's always dark, with no moon and stars illuminating light in the sky. I have no sense of direction. I don't know where I'm heading, or even if I'm moving anywhere. Some days the sea is calm and other days it's rough, rocking the boat side to side aggressively. I don't how long this journey is going to last, and sometimes I doubt there is even an end. Sometimes I feel this is it, forever living in this nightmare lost at sea.

However, there is one light. A tiny white dot in the distance, coming from a lighthouse. It has always been there, right from the start.

This light was there even on the hardest days of my journey. As I mentioned earlier, a person's spirit will always be stronger than an eating disorder. I didn't realise it at the time, as the voices were too loud to hear, that there was always a part of me never giving up hope. It was that light that give me the direction and strength to keep going – to believe I will one day arrive at the shore and leave the boat, the sea, the anorexia behind, and walk onto the chapter in my life, a stronger version of myself.

Success is an accumulation of many failures.

Suzanne Baker – carer of two daughters with anorexia nervosa

Please know that carers do not cause eating disorders, and eating disorders are not choices but serious, biologically influenced, illnesses. Your loved one is in the grips of a brain disorder. The rationale of a starved brain is not the rationale of well-nourished brain. You may see really bizarre behaviours – the result of starvation or malnourishment to the brain. There is no recovery without full weight restoration and nutritional rehabilitation. Food is your loved one's medicine and meal support is hugely important.

Hold firm against the illness – all members of the treatment team need to stand strong together – clinicians and carers. Eating disorders love gaps through which to wriggle – do not give them any. Learn how to tolerate distress – the anxiety of challenging behaviours can cause chaos in a home. Do not engage with the eating disorder, and repeat mantras in the face of huge distress, such as "I know you are scared but this food is your medicine", on repeat. When your loved one is calm, this can be when the eating disorder is finding a gap to wriggle through – know that when your loved one is kicking back against treatment this is actually when the eating disorder is being challenged. Remember that your loved one may have no idea just how ill they are, due to their brain being compromised and they are not not engaging with treatment, nor are they not motivated to recover. They are likely to be hugely terrified and not getting the "correct" signals from their brain.

Families are not to blame, and can be the patients' and providers' best allies in treatment.

An eating disorder diagnosis is a health crisis that disrupts personal and family functioning.

You know your loved one the best and are the vital link to the person pre illness. Seek out resources that will empower you to become a more effective caregiver. You won't know the questions to ask, so reach out to other carers who have walked in your shoes, and who are so generous in sharing what worked for them. There are many third sector organisations that offer forums and educational programmes. You simply don't know what you don't know, and don't even know the questions to ask.

If you think there is a problem, it is highly likely that there is an illness present; do not accept a "wait and see" approach. Recovery is possible, with early and timely intervention being key.

Fit your own oxygen mask first – recovery from an eating disorder is a marathon and not a sprint and takes many years, and do not ever feel guilty for taking time out for yourself. Supporting someone with an eating disorder is often like living with a terrorist – it is terrifying.

Keep the person pre illness at the forefront of your mind – they are still there inside, hugely terrified deep down and crying out for help, but not being able to advocate for this due to the strength of these illnesses.

Eating disorders affect the whole family unit and siblings can be hugely affected. Spend time with them, reassure them that their sibling is suffering from an illness and everyone is doing their best to make them well. Ask friends or family to have them over for meals to try and give them a bit of "normal" life and time away from their changed home environment. Try and have time when all your focus is on them. When an eating disorder lands in a family, it can be like a bomb going off, resulting in huge chaos, distress, and anguish – know that this is normal and not a reflection of your family.

Ask the person treating your loved one, "Do you believe that full recovery is possible?" We would ask this for all biologically based illnesses; eating disorders are no different.

Never, ever, give up hope. Hold the hope for your loved one, when they are not able to hold it for themselves. Recovery is possible, at any age and stage.

Never, ever give up hope. Hold the hope for your loved one, when they are not able to hold it for themselves. Recovery is possible, at any age and stage.

Anny Johnson – lived experience of binge eating disorder

My advice to anyone at the start of this journey is to be open, be kind and patient with yourself, and take one step at a time. Before you know it, you'll take a look back and realise just how far you've come.

Christina Taylor – lived experience of anorexia nervosa

My partner and I would say that it's equally important for the partner of an eating disorder sufferer to have someone to talk to openly as much as the sufferer. My children know I have an eating disorder and they are very proud of my recovery, coming along to talks that I do sometimes. We talk very honestly, but age-appropriately, about mental health and eating. As a family, we talk about mental health in the same way as we would talk about physical health, and encourage our children to tell us about difficult feelings. One of the proudest days in my recovery was when I ate ice cream with my children and shared my food with them.

Marina – lived experience of bulimia nervosa

I have learned the power of a positive friendship group – my friends have been my rocks, and have not only been the place I can cry and feel safe expressing the often frustration and exhaustion at years of bulimia, but also have been who I laugh with and create amazing memories with, reminding me of all that is so much bigger and better than bulimia.

What works for some people might not work for others. We often shy away from talking about issues, out of worry it'll make others uncomfortable, but this is often not the case. Ask what our boundaries are, and respect these. Please look after yourselves, too, if supporting someone with an eating disorder, and highlight your own boundaries: friends aren't a substitute for therapists or formal support, and in supporting each other we need to look after ourselves.

Try not to engage with the eating disorder. The sad reality is, sometimes our eating disorder will try to drag friends into reinforcing negative behaviours. So, if someone is, e.g. talking about their weight, simply don't comment. You can even go as far as stating you're not going to facilitate this.

Check your own internalised behaviours, e.g. please don't talk about January diet fads. That said, your issues also matter. Friendship is a two-way relationship, so just because I myself am struggling, that doesn't mean I am not there for you. Some big don'ts are comments like "Just eat normally", etc.

At the end of the day, just keep being the friend, family member, or whoever else you are you've always been – and don't see me as just the eating disorder. You're friends with Marina, not with bulimia.

Dave Chawner – lived experience of anorexia nervosa

Eating disorders are serious, but that doesn't mean we have to be. Let's change the tone around mental health, let's look at the positive, rather than the negative. Let's engage people with fun and positivity rather than drippy, drab sob stories.

Laura Hanton – lived experience of anorexia nervosa

I wish I had some words of wisdom for those who are at the beginning of their recovery journey, but all I can say is that there really is no other option. You have to recover. You deserve more than a life consumed by an eating disorder. And, once you're out the other side, I promise that you will never look back. There is so much love and joy and adventure to be found in a world without anorexia – you just have to be brave, trust those around you, and take the leap.

Rochelle Rouse – carer of a daughter with anorexia nervosa

The reality is, there is no magic wand, or magic pill, no CAMHS team, specialist therapy, or support group that will make the eating disorder go away. No therapist is going to click a switch and make your child see reason. Treating an eating disorder requires months and years of relentless parent/carer devotion and determination. Your child has to gain weight to recover. Full stop. The sooner they do, the better the outcome. What that looks like for each child will vary hugely.

Anjali Heer – lived experience of other specified feeding or eating disorder

If I could offer one piece of advice to someone, it would be to not see recovery as a destination but view it as a journey to fall in love with. Despite the ups and downs and the hardships, each day you choose to pick yourself up and try again is you showing your strength. Never allow your eating disorder to manipulate you in thinking it's more powerful than you. Your bravery and strength to get through day by day is something to be valued. Do something compassionate for yourself each day, no matter how small. Self-love takes time, but with each time step towards it you will get there.

> Each day you choose to pick yourself up and try again is you showing your strength.

Kirsty Stapledon – lived experience of other specified feeding or eating disorder

Letting go of my eating disorder was difficult at first. My eating disorder was my way of coping, and letting it go meant facing my feelings, even the uncomfortable ones. This also meant I had to find "me" away from my eating disorder. This didn't mean forgetting my eating disorder ever happened, it just meant making sure I embraced all parts of me – my values, my loves, my loved ones – and all parts of my life. In some ways, my journey involved changing my relationship to my eating disorder. For example, I now use my lived experience to empathise with and help others in similar situations, through campaigning, awareness work, and in my role as a peer support worker ... and in sharing this story here!

Sophie Reindorp – lived experience of binge eating disorder

To anyone else who is feeling hopeless, alone, and tired of struggling, what I would say is, reach out and tell your GP what is happening for you. You may have to see a few different people before you get to the right place. The journey may be long and difficult, and the wait times can be excruciating. But you have the whole rest of your life waiting for you.

Chelsea Spencer – lived experience of rumination disorder

If I could travel back in time, I would get the person to fight for what they felt they needed and fight for a proper diagnosis, full support, and to have encouraged them to be honest, engage in treatment, and keep focused on a goal. The teams are there to try and help; do not take the first opportunity you get to go backwards or try to defy the rules just to see if anyone is paying attention. This behaviour not only hurts (may even kill) yourself, but it kills everyone else around you and intensifies stress and pressure. Do not lose friends, hope, or relationships over the strong will of the illness. Use your support network to fight and find a way forward.

Living is possible and, without food, you will have no fuel to give your body the energy, vibe, and soul it needs to live. Do not restrict your life to fit into little tick boxes the professionals demand you need to fit into to gain a specific label. You should never be put in a box. The box you are put in at the end of life should come at the end of a long life – one that is fun-filled, full of achievements, love and laughter, and endless possibilities. You are not your diagnosis; do not let it become you.

Chris Avenell – carer of a daughter with rumination disorder

I would say to a carer, at the beginning of this awful journey, trust your instinct, not the person you are supporting. The illness will make them lie to you. It's not them lying, it's the illness, so trust your instinct.

Trust your instinct, not the person you are supporting. The illness will make them lie to you. It's not them lying, it's the illness, so trust your instinct.

Sharon Miklosova – lived experience of binge eating disorder

If I could say one thing to someone reading this and realising they might have an eating disorder, too, it would be to keep trying. Not every treatment works for everyone. It can take trial and error to find the right one for you. But, if you keep trying, I'm hopeful you will find your way to recovery. It has taken me nearly a decade to find the combination of different disciplines and techniques that work for me. And it's been worth it. Recovery has given me so much: the freedom to discover who I am without constant thoughts about food; the chance to make lasting, genuine relationships with people who like me for me; the clarity to see that my true value was never about how I looked or a number on a scale; and the courage to finally live my life on my terms.

GLOSSARY

Dr Elizabeth McNaught,
Professor Janet Treasure, and Jess Griffiths

Acceptance and commitment therapy (ACT) A type of mindful psychotherapy that helps you stay focused on the present moment and accept thoughts and feelings without judgment.

Amphetamines Stimulants which act on the central nervous system. These may be prescribed by a healthcare professional for the treatment of disorders such as attention deficit hyperactivity disorder, or they may be abused as a recreational drug in substance abuse.

Antipsychotics Medication which may be prescribed to treat psychosis; some are also licensed to treat other mental health conditions.

Anxiety disorders A group of mental health conditions with a central feature of anxiety, out of proportion to what would be considered normal. These include social phobia, panic disorder, and generalised anxiety disorder.

Atrophy The wasting away, and reduction, of body tissue.

Attention deficit hyperactivity disorder (ADHD) A disorder characterised by inattention, hyperactivity, and impulsive behaviour. People may feel restless and have difficulty concentrating or completing tasks, which has an impact on their life and functioning. ADHD is often diagnosed in children, but is increasingly recognised in adults.

Autism spectrum disorder (ASD) A developmental disability affecting how people interact and communicate. They may show restrictive or repetitive behaviours, over-focused interests and activities, and be particularly sensitive to stimulation (e.g. taste, touch, sight, sound). This is a spectrum, so is experienced in different ways by different people.

Bipolar disorder A type of mood disorder which is characterised by periods of low mood and periods of abnormally elevated mood (manic or hypomanic). Some people may experience psychotic episodes during their illness, with the presence of hallucinations and/or delusions.

Black, Asian, and minority ethnic (BAME) An umbrella term, common in the United Kingdom, used to describe non-white ethnicitqties.

Body mass index (BMI) A measure used to assess if someone is a healthy weight. It is calculated by dividing someone's weight by their height (in meters) squared. People may be classified as underweight, normal weight, overweight, obese, or extremely obese.

CAMHS (Child and Adolescent Mental Health Service) The name for the NHS services that assess and treat young people with emotional, behavioural, or mental health difficulties.

Collateral history The gaining of information from a third party in the assessment of a disorder, typically from a close family member such as a parent, carer, spouse, or sibling.

Comorbidity The presence of other health conditions (physical or psychological) which are presenting, or co-existing, at the same time as the primary condition.

Concordance rate A measure which is often used in twin studies, to determine the role of genetics and the environment in the presence of a condition or trait. It is reported as the proportion of pairs of twins that share a trait or condition.

Contraindication A condition or circumstance that suggests or indicates that a particular technique or drug should not be used in the case in question.

Diagnostic and statistical manual of mental disorders, fifth edition (DSM-5) A manual published, in 2013, by the American Psychiatric Association (APA) giving guidance on the diagnostic criteria for a wide range of mental illnesses.

Dietitian A health care professional who has trained and specialised in managing nutritional problems.

Dietary restraint A term used to describe the attempt to restrict what one eats

Diuretics Medication which is prescribed by a health care professional to increase urine production and reduce body fluid and salt levels. This is often used in the treatment of high blood pressure and heart failure.

Electrocardiogram (ECG) This is a medical test conducted to assess the electrical activity of the heart. It can also assess the heart rate and rhythm and may identify structural disorders within the heart.

Enteral feeding In medical settings this often described the process of using a tube placed into the gastrointestinal tract for the provision of nutrition. Examples include a nasogastric tube (tube placed from the nose to the stomach) and a gastrostomy (a tube in placed through the skin to the stomach).

Fat talk Talking in a negative way about your own or others body weight, shape or eating habits.

Formulation An approach that draws on psychological theory and research to provide a framework for describing a client's problems or needs, how it developed and is being maintained.

Genome wide association studies Studies that look across the genome for genetic markers which show a level of association with a condition.

Gillick competence A term used in medical law to decide whether a child (a person under 16 years of age) is able to consent to their own medical treatment, without the need for parental permission or knowledge.

Heritability estimates A measure which ranges from 0 to 1, defining how much of a trait or condition has developed due to genetic or environmental factors.

Impulse control disorders A mental illness with a key feature being impulsivity. People have a tendency to act in a rushed, reactive way without prior thought.

Incidence A measure of new cases of an illness developing during a defined period of time.

Inpatient A patient who resides in hospital while under treatment.

International Classification of Disease 11th Revision (ICD-11) Developed by the World Health Organization (WHO) and is a globally recognised classification system detailing the diagnostic criteria for both physical illnesses and mental illnesses.

Laxatives Medication which are used to aid the emptying of bowels, there are different types which work in different ways (bulk forming increase the fluid and thus bulk of the stool making them easier to pass, stimulant act on the bowel wall to improve emptying). These can be bought over the counter or via a prescription from a health care professional.

Malnutrition A medical state which develops due to an incorrect nutritional intake. This may be undernutrition which occurs due to too little nutritional intake, or overnutrition which is due to excessive nutritional intake.

Mood disorders   A group of mental health conditions with a central feature being a disturbance in mood, this may be a low mood or elevated mood. Conditions include depression and bipolar disorder.

Mortality rate   The number of deaths in a defined time period and defined population.

Multidisciplinary team (MDT)   A group of professionals from different areas of health care, who work together to provide joined up care in supporting people with complex care needs.

Nasogastric feeding   A tube is inserted through the nose, down the throat and esophagus, and into the stomach. It can be used to give drugs, liquids, and liquid food. Giving food through a nasogastric tube is a type of enteral nutrition. Also called gastric feeding tube and NG tube.

National Institute for Health and Care Excellence (NICE)   Independent, public body which provides a range of services including the production of advice and evidence based guidelines for health care professionals.

Neurodiversity   Examples of developmental conditions such as autistic spectrum disorder or attention deficit disorder which include diversity in cognitive, emotional, social and behavioural traits (e.g. dyslexia, extreme shyness, impulsivity or compulsivity).

Neuroplasticity   The brains' ability to adapt following interaction with the world around us. The brain may grow, change its structure, and make new connections following life events and stimulation.

Obsessive compulsive disorder   A mental health condition characterised by the presence of obsessions (negative, intrusive thoughts or images) and compulsions (repetitive behaviours carried out to placate the anxiety or negative emotions brought about by the obsessions).

Orthorexia   An unhealthy fixation on eating healthy food, people may perceive food and clean or pure and dirty and impure, this has an impact on their life and functioning.

Outpatient   A patient who attends a hospital for treatment without staying there overnight.

Overevaluation of weight and shape   Judging the self-worth exclusively or predominantly in terms of a person's shape, weight, and their control.

Personality disorders A group of disorders which have a negative effect on people's behaviours and thought processes. This influences their functioning and relationships.

Picky eating A common eating behaviour seen in young children where they avoid foods they dislike based on taste, texture, smell etc. This does not cause malnutrition or have a negative effect on functioning and often resolves with age.

Prevalence The number of cases of an illness, this may be at a specified point in time (point prevalence) or over a defined period of time (period prevalence).

Psychoeducation An evidence-based therapeutic intervention for patients and their loved ones that provides information and support to better understand and cope with illness.

Refeeding syndrome A medical condition which develops following the reinstatement of nutrition after a period of food restriction. This results in a disturbance in the bodies electrolytes which can be fatal if not managed appropriately.

Relapse prevention A cognitive– behavioural approach with the goal of identifying and addressing high-risk situations for relapse and assisting individuals in maintaining desired behavioural changes.

Remission The temporary or permanent reduction (or disappearance) of an illness.

Selective serotonin reuptake inhibitor (SSRI) A type of anti-depressant which may be prescribed by a health care professional often in the treatment of depression or anxiety. They are thought to work by increasing the levels of serotonin in the brain having a positive effect on mental health.

Self-harm The secretive, intentional injuring of one's own body (e.g. cutting, burning, scratching) often done as a way of managing negative feelings and emotions. Following the injury people may feel a sense of relief.

Specialist eating disorder service A service providing specialist psychological support, advice and treatment for people with moderate to severe eating disorders.

Substance abuse The misuse of drugs (e.g. opiates, cocaine) or alcohol which may have significant and detrimental effects on people's functioning and or physical health. People may feel unable to control of limit their substance use and go on to suffer from addiction.

Talking therapies Psychological therapies, provided by the NHS, for the treatment of some mental health conditions including depression and anxiety. A range of therapies may be offered including guided self help and cognitive behavioural therapy. This may be provided with self-help material, virtually, or in person.

Triggers A trigger is a stimulus that elicits a reaction. In the context of mental illness, "trigger" is often used to mean something that brings on or worsens symptoms.

Type 1 diabetes A medical condition which develops due to the bodies inability to produce insulin, this results in raised blood sugar and medical complications secondary to this.

Weight restoration The process of eating disorder recovery refers to an individual reaching weight stability. This means that an individual reaches a weight that is healthy for them, meets their nutritional and growth needs, and is a weight that they are able to maintain long-term.

INDEX